The trial was approaching in the summer of 2005 and I was a nervous wreck. My skills, competence, and most importantly, my integrity, were being impugned. I was outraged at Dr. Z's written report. My entire future was at stake against an opponent who was not interested in fairness, justice, or the truth. Suzan and I arranged for child care and we traveled to Harrisburg in July for the two-day trial.

At the trial, I finally met Dr. Z in person. He extended his hand to me and without thought, I shook it by default. I immediately regretted it. That single act of civility has haunted me since then. How could I possibly have accepted the hand of someone who was intentionally trying to destroy me without regard for the truth? I sacrificed my self-respect in that instant in the name of good manners. I have not been able to come to terms with that, even after all these years. It was truly a life-changing action for me. I was already 48 years old at the time, but I learned a lot about myself and grew up quite a bit that day. Courtesy and consideration are important but should not be rendered to those who engage in unethical behavior.

The trial then commenced. The hearing examiner allowed Dr. Z's testimony, despite his lack of qualifications. During the trial, Dr. Z continued to make ridiculous assertions that demonstrated his lack of knowledge of the current practice of medicine and more specifically the practice of rheumatology. This was not surprising as he had no rheumatology training, but it was distressing nonetheless. His oral testimony continued to demonstrate that he had not read my chart thoroughly. He repeatedly drew conclusions criticizing my care, which were not substantiated by the facts of the case. He was on the witness stand for a day and a half. It was excruciating to listen to him with the thought that the hearing examiner might find his testimony credible.

My expert witness was board certified in pain management. After he refuted the nonsense spewed by Dr. Z, it was my turn to take the stand. I did so with great apprehension and was visibly shaking as I sat there. The prosecuting attorney grilled me, but I had an answer for every question she posed. My chart was well documented on every challenge that she raised. My testimony must have been very damaging to their case against me, as I was only on the stand for 20 minutes, compared to the day and a half that Dr. Z had testified.

Then it was over. I was numb. I waited nervously for a result and tried to resume normalcy.

Rheum for Improvement

Rheum for Improvement

The Evolution of a Health-Care Advocate

Mark Lopatin, MD

Universal-Publishers
Irvine • Boca Raton

Rheum for Improvement:
The Evolution of a Health-Care Advocate

Universal Publishers, Inc.
Irvine • Boca Raton
USA • 2022
www.Universal-Publishers.com

ISBN: 978-1-62734-376-3 (pbk.)
ISBN: 978-1-62734-377-0 (ebk.)

For permission to photocopy or use material electronically from this work, please access www.copyright.com or contact the Copyright Clearance Center, Inc. (CCC) at 978-750-8400. CCC is a not-for-profit organization that provides licenses and registration for a variety of users. For organizations that have been granted a photocopy license by the CCC, a separate system of payments has been arranged.

Typeset by Medlar Publishing Solutions Pvt Ltd, India
Cover design by Ivan Popov

Library of Congress Cataloging-in-Publication Data

Names: Lopatin, Mark, 1957- author.
Title: Rheum for improvement : the evolution of a health care advocate / Mark Lopatin, MD.
Description: Irvine : Universal Publishers, 2022. | Includes bibliographical references.
Identifiers: LCCN 2021052445 (print) | LCCN 2021052446 (ebook) | ISBN 9781627343763 (paperback) | ISBN 9781627343770 (ebook)
Subjects: LCSH: Patient advocacy. | Public relations.
Classification: LCC R727.45 .L67 2022 (print) | LCC R727.45 (ebook) | DDC 610--dc23/eng/20211227
LC record available at https://lccn.loc.gov/2021052445
LC ebook record available at https://lccn.loc.gov/2021052446

TABLE OF CONTENTS

PART III RESOLUTION

Introduction

On page 4 of his novel, *11/22/1963*, Stephen King writes "Life turns on a dime." Based on my experiences, he was 100% correct. There are so many times in my career where a simple phone call, chance encounter, or something else took the course of my life on a dramatic detour. Even when life is going well, a car accident, a new cancer diagnosis, or a malpractice lawsuit can acutely change someone's life in a negative direction. Spoiler alert: It was not either of the first two that changed me from a mind-your-own-business type of physician into an outspoken advocate for health-care reform. Most of my "turn on a dime" events have been positive ones, but some like the latter have thrown me into a tailspin. I therefore have tried to consciously appreciate all that I have, as it may not be there tomorrow. This is something I taught my daughters at a young age as I explained that all of the blessings we have in our lives—loved ones, friends, family, health, material possessions, and so on—are not worth much if we take them for granted and are unable to appreciate them.

One of the recurring themes in this book is how much I didn't know, and how much I had to learn. My naiveté and lack of understanding of so many important things are well reflected in this book. That is why I consider myself an unlikely health-care advocate. Fortunately, anger is a powerful instigator. I was capable of learning and was motivated to act on what I learned in an attempt to effect change. I am still learning now even after retirement.

The most important messages in this book, however, are the critical importance of humanity in medicine and the sacred nature of the patient-physician relationship. The patient is listed first because they are the most important consideration in health care. We need to recognize that patients are people, not simply their diseases. Likewise, we must recognize that physicians are human as well, with all the attributes and flaws that non-physicians have.

Although I had known that I wanted to be a doctor from a young age to "help people," I really was clueless as to what that cliché actually entailed. Samuel Shem, in his novel, *The House of God*, talks about "being with patients," (that is, the ability to empathize with and relate to patient experiences) as the essence of medicine. Being a doctor is not simply about ordering tests, making diagnoses, writing prescriptions, and moving on to the next patient. The relationship between patient and physician is the crux of health care, or at least it should be, but it is being destroyed in so many ways by those who seek to control the health-care dollar. We are losing the humanity in medicine to corporate powers, and even to the government. Regulations such as prior authorization as well as a slew of acronyms, such as MACRA, MIPS, MOC, and PBMs inhabit the health-care landscape to the detriment of patients.

As an example, let's look at how documentation has exceeded actual patient care in level of importance. Documenting what you have done as a physician is essential, but it has gotten entirely out of hand. I have jokingly commented that my degree should be changed from an MD to a DEO, as I have become a glorified data entry operator. Getting the right answer no longer matters. Instead the focus is on whether a physician has shown their work and appropriately justified the reasoning for a particular diagnostic test or treatment to a third party. Documentation that is unsatisfactory to a third party may mean denial of a particular test or treatment or result in inadequate reimbursement. The electronic health record (EHR) has become nothing more than a billing tool. The price we pay is that the more time physicians spend documenting, the less time we spend engaging patients.

A typical office visit consists of six parts:

1. Exchanging pleasantries with the patient.
2. Gathering information via history, physical exam, and review of data.
3. Processing that information to formulate a plan of action.
4. Implementing the plan by ordering the necessary tests or treatment.
5. Communicating that plan to the patient.
6. Documenting the plan in the patient's chart.

Physicians typically have 15 minutes to accomplish all of this for a follow-up patient.

Documentation should be focused on explaining a physician's thought processes, but instead the emphasis has been placed on quantifying data.

For example, as a rheumatologist, one of the key things I must assess is pain. Pain is subjective and cannot be quantified using a 1–10 numerical scale. Physicians, however, are forced to use such a scale to satisfy one of the insurer's criteria for reimbursement. The problem is that one person's "8" is another person's "2". Furthermore, pain levels are different at different times, in different places, and for different conditions. Physicians are expected to provide one number at each visit to quantify a patient's pain experience.

What happens, then, with a patient whose underlying chronic conditions are stable, but whose pain level fluctuates in relation to other acute issues? This actually happened to a patient of mine with stable rheumatoid arthritis (RA) and fibromyalgia, who was denied long-term insurance because the underwriter stated that her fibromyalgia was worsening based on her pain scores. As I explained to the underwriter in my letter:

> In August 2016, her pain level was eight. But this eight referred to pain in her thumb from osteoarthritis. That progress note also documented that her fibromyalgia was improving, yet her pain score went up because of the thumb. In June 2016, her pain score was ten, but this was referable to an injury to her hamstring and had nothing to do with her fibromyalgia or rheumatoid arthritis.

The underwriter was absolutely clueless as to the use of pain scores. The fact that her chronic conditions were stable and that the pain in each case was due to something other than her chronic conditions did not matter. I spent several hours writing the above letter and communicating at various times with her financial advisor to try to resolve the problem, but to no avail. Despite my efforts, the insurer continued to deny her application by relying solely on pain scores, and she ultimately needed to consult an attorney. All of this because of the mandated need to quantify pain by recording one number in the chart, combined with the inability or unwillingness of an insurer to understand that one number is an essentially worthless assessment of a patient's condition. Yes, bureaucracy harms patients.

One of the key elements in this case was whether the patient's pain was getting worse. Physicians are also routinely required by insurers to not only provide a number to define a patient's pain level but also to document if a patient's pain is better or worse. The question is, since when? Since the initial diagnosis? Since their last office visit? Since last week? Since yesterday? How do I record the pain level for a given condition, if it is better than it was last week, worse than it was yesterday, and about the same as it was at her last office visit a month ago? How should I document improvement when the pain in one joint is better, but pain in another joint is worse? What if the pain from her rheumatoid arthritis is worse, but her pain from fibromyalgia is better? Am I expected to document the pain at each visit, in each location, in each time frame, and for each condition? The amount of time it would take for me to document all of that would preclude me from actually providing medical care. Time spent documenting measures such as this is time not spent truly caring for patients.

Even documenting the diagnosis has become difficult. Physicians must use an alpha-numeric code for each diagnosis, and the number of codes expanded from 13,000 to 68,000 in 2015. These diagnostic codes often must be specified based on factors such as onset of the problem, an underlying cause to the problem, chronic versus acute, with or without complication, left versus right, initial versus subsequent visit, and so on.

One of my patients had been diagnosed with rheumatoid arthritis in 1972. This new coding system, however, would not allow me to use rheumatoid arthritis as the diagnosis. Instead, I was obligated to specifically designate whether a particular blood test was positive or negative. This test is useful in making the initial diagnosis, but it is not a test that is usually done thereafter. To code her visit properly, I had to look through 44 years of progress notes and labs trying to find this one lab result that no longer had any relevance to her care. The time that I spent buried in the computer looking for meaningless data could have been better spent focusing on the patient. Since I could not find the result, I had to order a new blood test with no benefit to the patient, just to satisfy the government's coding specifications.

One study in the *Annals of Internal Medicine* looked at reports from 57 U.S. physicians in family medicine, internal medicine, cardiology, and orthopedics who were observed for 430 hours.[1] Twenty-one of these physicians also completed after-hours diaries. The study showed that during a typical day, physicians spent almost twice as much time on electronic health records and desk work as they did on direct clinical face time with patients. Even while with the patient in the exam room, physicians spent more than one third of their time on documentation and only 52.9% on direct clinical face time. If we assume an office visit is 15 minutes, that means that five and a half of them are spent on the electronic health record, and only eight minutes are spent on direct patient care. Furthermore, physicians reported spending on average an extra one to two hours each day engaging in after-hours computer and clerical tasks. Another retrospective study of 142 physicians done at the University of Wisconsin[2] revealed that for a typical 11.4 hour workday, 5.9 hours, or more than half of a physician's time, was spent on documentation.

This excessive need for documentation detracts from physicians' ability to care for patients properly. The key word here is "excessive." Documentation is important, but not to this degree. As noted by one physician, "Dr. Mom," on the medical blog "Sermo,"

> Am I the only doctor who is sick and tired of being told how much my time is worth? I have to justify my time and substance of visits for each payment. I am spending more time documenting my visits than I am seeing my patients. If I see a patient for 30 minutes, I have to document for 30 minutes why I spent that time. I get the distinct honor of coding the assessments and then I get to code quality measures. AND LORD FORBID I DON'T—then I don't meet the standard of care. Just whose standard is that?

Furthermore, much of the documentation is required for billing purposes, rather than patient care. Doctors Christopher Notte and Neil Skolnick have noted, "The patient's chart, once considered a sacred text containing the key inflection points in a patient's story, has become merely a filing cabinet in which to stuff every piece of data about the patient no matter how mundane or trivial." The demand for documentation results in long computer-generated notes that contain little practical information. It is not uncommon for a 16-page progress note to contain only one paragraph of useful information.

We have seen tremendous advances in science and technology, but the take-home message needs to be that being a physician and caring for patients is inherently a human experience. This is where we need to be placing our focus, not on documentation for documentation's sake. How a physician relates to their patient may well be the most critical aspect of easing the patient's suffering and is not something that can be quantified. The corporate takeover of medicine is extracting the humanity out of health care at an alarming rate, resulting in unprecedented levels of physician burnout. I assert that the best doctors are the ones who genuinely care about their patients as opposed to the ones who know the most. Medicine needs to be filled with "H"s: Helping, Humor, and Humility as corollaries to Healing, but Humanity remains the most important "H." Hopefully this message will come through in this book. The need for documentation is just one example of how humanity, and therefore health care, is being compromised.

PART I

EVOLUTION

Chapter 1

Beginnings

In the beginning, I was completely clueless. The year was 1975. The top movies that year were *Jaws* and *One Flew Over the Cuckoo's Nest.* "Love Will Keep Us Together" by Captain & Tennille was the top song, and gas was 57 cents per gallon. I was 18 years old but a very young 18 years old. I had just graduated high school in the top 1% of my class. I was book-smart but lacked life experience. Nerd, geek, dweeb—take your pick for the proper word that was applicable. The only job I had ever had was as a karate instructor, and I simply did not have the relationship skills necessary to be successful at teaching others. I had started karate lessons five years earlier at the insistence of my father after I had had the crap knocked out of me in a fight. It was the only fight I ever had.

I was a late bloomer. I only weighed 140 pounds when I graduated high school. My first girlfriend did not appear until after high school graduation, and she only lasted that summer, before we went to separate colleges. I was about to enter the University of Pennsylvania for pre-med.

I was oblivious to the world, having grown up in the amniotic fluid of a sheltered middle-class existence in the suburbs of Philadelphia. I remember being sent home early from first grade, but nothing else, on the day JFK was assassinated. The tumultuous events of 1968; the assassinations of Martin Luther King, Jr. and Robert Kennedy, the war in Vietnam, and racism as exemplified by George Wallace, barely registered on my radar as an 11-year-old. The Kent State shootings occurred in 1970, when I was 13 and did not move the needle for me. Even Watergate, a few years later, did not attract my interest or arouse my curiosity. In 1975, the war in Vietnam finally ended, but to me that did not matter because I knew very little about it anyway. I knew nothing of racism and politics. Although I am Jewish, I had never experienced anti-Semitism. I did not know the difference between a Democrat and a Republican, nor did I care. I would be able to vote for the first time in the 1976 election, but even having that privilege did not spark my interest. It would not be until the early 2000s that politics would register on my radar. I had no idea of what was going on in the world around me.

Growing up, my passions were sports, especially the four major Philadelphia sports teams. I played street hockey and football with the other kids in the neighborhood. I was an avid hockey fan. I cried when the Flyers missed the playoffs by four seconds at the end of the 1971–72 season. I played tennis and golf regularly with my dad. I knew the layout of Valley Forge golf course by heart. As a senior in high school, my classes were often done for the day by 11:30 a.m., and I would sneak on to Merion with a friend of mine to get in a few holes here or there. The Flyers had just won the Stanley Cup for the second time, and I kept a record of every game that season, listing the final score, goaltender, and losing team. Not surprisingly, my high school calculus teacher labeled me a "Flyers nut" when he signed my yearbook. I followed the rules and deferred to authority. Skipping school was unheard of for me, but somehow I found a way to assuage my guilt enough to attend the Flyers' parades in 1974 and 1975. I was such a fan that my first year in college, I took it upon myself to visit Joe Watson, a Flyers defenseman, in a local hospital after he was injured. I can only imagine what he must have thought of this 18-year-old who showed up at his hospital room to meet him in person. It would not be the last time I presented myself to a complete stranger to achieve a goal.

Growing up, we had season tickets to the Eagles, first at Franklin Field and then Veterans Stadium, and I loved them despite their lack of success in the 1970s. In 1975, the Phillies were about to be good again. The 76ers told me that they owed me one. Sports was my focus.

I had no way of knowing in 1975 what the future would hold and the unexpected paths my life would take. There was no way to predict that I would become political, or that I would someday be leading a protest outside a local hospital carrying a sign advising patients that if they were sick, to call their lawyer, rather than their doctor. An AP photographer recorded the event and it was featured in *Time* and *USA Today*.

Nor did I know that I would be interviewed for a *New York Times* article[3] criticizing how pharmacies operate, or that I would write numerous articles and/or op-eds for newspapers across Pennsylvania and in national physician blogs regarding our broken health-care system. I could not imagine that I would be asked to do national podcasts, addressing issues that compromise the care that patients receive. I could not foresee that I would serve first as president and then chairman of the board of my county medical society and also serve on the board of trustees for both the Pennsylvania Medical Society and their political action committee. I had no way to envision that I would be afforded the opportunity to speak at the Library of Congress or serve on the National Physicians Council for Healthcare Policy. I did not know that I would meet and communicate with many other physician advocates from across the country as well as many legislators. Social media was unimaginable at that time, and so was my ultimate future as an advocate for health-care reform. In 1975 that concept was beyond my realm of comprehension, with good reason.

At age 18, I viewed medicine as a noble profession. Doctors were highly respected in the community. Marcus Welby was an icon, appearing on television every Tuesday night to ease yet another patient's suffering. There was no mention of the corruption that exists in health care. I had not yet learned that some physicians will say anything, even in a court of law, where the truth is required, or that lawyers could bring a case against you simply because you were a treating physician. It was a foreign idea to me that when the state board of medicine has an agenda, the facts of the case don't really matter. It was truly a rude awakening for me when I experienced these realities.

I did not yet realize that many would find it acceptable for those without a medical license, medical degree, or medical training to be able to practice medicine, and that some corporate entities would even promote that. Abbreviations such as MOC, MACRA, MIPS, or PBMs were not yet part of my lingo. Scope of practice was a foreign concept. I could not conceive that I would one day testify in Washington, D.C., regarding the sham that maintenance of certification has become. I had no way to know that middlemen and bureaucrats would hijack health care for their own financial gains. There was an awful lot about practicing medicine that I had yet to learn or could even imagine. My ideals were about to be shattered!

At that time, I simply anticipated the wonderful feelings that come from helping people. I had no idea of forthcoming legal cases or that I would experience a form of post-traumatic stress disorder (PTSD) as a result of fraudulent testimony against me that threatened my career. I never considered the feelings of helplessness when a patient suffers and you can't fix them; the introspection that comes when a patient is angry or upset with you; or the despair that sets in when you feel you may have actually done something that might have hurt someone else.

I was about to get schooling in more than just medicine. I was about to get an education in life and in myself that would take more than 40 years. It is still ongoing.

In 1975, I headed off to college armed with a letter from my older brother with life advice regarding the future. I continued to bask in the glow of my naiveté. While in college, I joined a fraternity. I got drunk for the first time in my life. I tried marijuana but never anything stronger. During my entire four years in college, I only had one girlfriend, and that was only for a total of two to three months. I watched a stacked Phillies team fail to win the pennant for three straight years from 1976 to 1978. I celebrated Hey Day and Skimmer Weekend at Penn each year. I "drank a highball" and "raised a toast to dear old Penn" at college football games. I watched Penn go to the NCAA final four in 1979. Mostly, however, I spent college taking science classes and studying in preparation for medical school.

During my sophomore year, I got a job working as a lab technician at Lankenau Hospital. This was my first occupational foray into the world of health care. One of my colleagues there later became my roommate in med school and a groomsman at my wedding. *Saturday Night Live* was all the rage, and with some friends, I made a movie detailing what would happen to Mr. Bill if he came to our lab to get his blood drawn. This was 1979. AIDS was unknown at the time, and we used real blood to illustrate Mr. Bill's travails. The world was innocent, or to be more accurate, I was.

I applied to medical school and was accepted to one in Philly and one in Pittsburgh. Naturally, I chose to stay close to home and attended the Medical College of Pennsylvania (MCP). MCP initially was founded in 1850 as the Female Medical College of Pennsylvania and became known as the Women's Medical College in 1867.[4] It was the first medical school in the world authorized to award women the MD degree. It ultimately became co-ed in 1970 and was renamed the Medical College of Pennsylvania. It was not well known as an academic institute. Instead, its strength was in its diversity, attracting students who were more well-rounded rather than simply accepting those with the highest grades and highest scores on their Medical College Admission Test.

Medical school was a whole new world for me, but most of my memories of that time are superficial ones. The first two years were merely an extension of college, albeit with much more material to learn. Of course, I never dissected a cadaver in anatomy lab as an undergraduate. We had many lectures every day, and each day a different student was required to take notes on the material. These notes would then be submitted to the instructor for accuracy and then distributed to the rest of the class for their study purposes. During my second year I had the opportunity to be the note taker for the session on history and physical exam. I have always liked a good pun and even more so, a bad one. I therefore proceeded to describe in my notes that when you ask a patient multiple questions about the abdomen and they answer no to all of them, they are referred to as "an abdominal no-man." The instructor at that time was the chief of medicine and he was not amused by my feeble attempt at humor. He was quite an intimidating figure to a second-year medical student. His response was to scrawl "NO" across my notes in large red letters. It was my first inkling that perhaps what I was doing should not be taken so lightheartedly. This man was a stickler for details, and he emphasized the commitment we needed to be making to medicine. As one example, he demanded that we do rectal exams on all patients admitted to the hospital, with the only two reasons for not doing so being no finger or no rectum. I did not appreciate him at that time. I thought him a curmudgeon with no sense of humor. Little did I realize the lesson he was teaching us in terms of being dedicated to our career path.

We played football or softball on the weekends. I was never much of a partier, although we sometimes would hit the local saloon after games, where I would slowly sip my one beer. I rarely finished it. When I was not studying, my outside life continued to revolve around sports. The year 1980 was a banner year for me, as all four Philadelphia sports teams went to the finals, with the Phillies winning the World Series. I had my first serious girlfriend, whom I had met at my brother's wedding. I was beginning to mature, but only a little.

We did not really start to see patients until my third year, and this was in the hospital setting. I did not have patients that I considered my own, and therefore did not really form any type of long-term relationships with them. I remember the name of my first patient that I saw in the hospital, but nothing more about her.

We learned how to conduct a history and physical as well as the diagnosis and management of different diseases. I remember being taught the importance of obtaining a complete history, including a sexual history, and practicing this skill on my patients. When I asked one patient if she was sexually active, she responded with, "No, I just lie there." Another patient must have thought he was Vanna White from *Wheel of Fortune*, as he reported trouble "moving his vowels." Yes, patients do say some unexpected things.

Residency provided new opportunities. For my first rotation, I was sentenced to go to West Park Hospital. West Park was a local community hospital that did not have a great reputation for teaching. The house staff held little respect for the attending physicians there. They were community doctors rather than academic doctors, and in our minds as hotshot residents, they knew very little. I feel quite differently now that I have been a community rheumatologist for 28 years, but I did not know any better at the time. I complained to the director of our residency program about having to start my training there. I wanted to go to a more powerful affiliate hospital for my first rotation where I could learn more. She taught me a very valuable lesson by explaining that my education and my future depended much more on me than on where I did my rotations. This was something I took to heart, so off I went to West Park. I learned medicine but also the importance of showing respect to those attending physicians whom I held in such low regard. That point was driven home when a nurse informed me that a patient I was seeing had an elevated blood pressure that I needed to address. My blunt response was, "No wonder his blood pressure is up. Look who his surgeon is."

That surgeon happened to be standing directly behind me at the time. He never said a word to me and I am guessing that he did not hear what I had said, but I was mortified. It was an example of how words can matter a great deal. I escaped without harm in this case and learned something valuable in the process.

Other hospitals taught me other lessons. Computers were just beginning to come into vogue at that time, and Frankford Hospital was using them so that staff could easily obtain patient information, usually lab results. Prior to this, if a doctor wanted to get a lab result, they needed to call the lab and wait on hold while someone found the result. With the computers, one could simply log in to the computer to get said results. The only problem with this was that administration did not see fit to give computer access to house staff, only to attending physicians and nurses. Now when we wanted to get lab results, instead of calling the lab, we would interrupt one of the nurses, and they would stop what they were doing to log in to the computer to provide us with the results. We did not always want to be bothering the nurses for this mundane task, so eventually one of my colleagues and I simply asked some of the nurses for their passwords so we could get results more expeditiously. We did not know, however, that the computer recorded every time we logged in, and suspicion was soon aroused when it was discovered that these nurses were accessing the computer at all hours of the day and night, even when they were not working. We were called on the carpet for this and almost got thrown out of our residency. However, the other residents rallied against this injustice, questioning why access to lab results was not given to the house staff in the first place, as we were the ones who needed it most. The issue was ultimately dropped, although not without quite a bit of anxiety.

It registered with me that advocacy can make a difference. I did not realize at the time the importance of that lesson, but I unconsciously stored it away for later use.

Then there was the VA, the Veterans Administration Hospital. We sarcastically called it the VA spa. It was anything but. I have stated many times, somewhat tongue in cheek, that the only reason we were asked to rotate through the VA was so that we would have unusual stories to tell later in life. Given that it was a government-run facility, the bureaucracy should not have been surprising. The day-to-day operations there astounded me.

Let's start with the "anti-nurse," as she was known to the house staff. She was a middle-aged nurse with tenure who clearly did not like the house staff and did everything she could to annoy and antagonize us. The nickname "anti-nurse" was analogous to the Anti-Christ. She was the exact opposite of what a nurse should be.

There were numerous examples. It is amazing how many times a patient's IV would just happen to stop working within an hour or two of a resident trying to get a few hours of sleep. We eventually adopted the strategy of checking every single IV before we went to bed at two or three o'clock in the morning, but it did not matter. One of the IVs that was working fine at 1:30 a.m. invariably seemed to stop running at 3:00 a.m., which meant we had to wake up, get out of bed, put our shoes on, and go the floor to replace the IV. Frequently, when we got to the patient's room, the IV was running without a problem, so we simply trudged back to the on-call room to try to get back to sleep. There never seemed to be a problem with IVs during the day, only at night.

Once, I received a call in the middle of the night to advise me that my patient's temperature was normal. When I asked the anti-nurse why she had woken me up to inform me of this, her response was, "I just thought you would want to know." At 3:00 a.m.? One of my colleagues once got a phone call in the middle of the night informing him that a constipated patient for whom he had ordered a laxative, had just had a large bowel movement. I routinely got calls for the next day's medication orders. Oftentimes, the dosage would depend on the results of the morning labs, so there was no way I could answer the question in the middle of the night. I would get phone calls waking me up asking for orders for a patient's lunch the next day. There was no reason this question needed to be asked in the middle of the night as opposed to the next morning.

The pièce de résistance occurred one morning when one of my confused patients decided he wanted to be a urologist and proceeded to yank out his Foley catheter. A Foley catheter is inserted through the penis into the bladder, with a small balloon that is blown up in the bladder to keep it in place. Before removing it, the balloon needs to be deflated as it will not fit through the urethra. My patient, however, did not understand that and simply gave it a strong jerk. When I reached him, blood was spewing from his penis, and I needed another set of hands immediately. I called for the anti-nurse, who refused to help. She informed me that she was "busy giving morning report." I did the best I could under the circumstances, and finally got the situation under control. Her refusal to help me compromised the patient's care. It would not be the last time that I saw behavior that negatively affected patient care, by people who had other agendas.

It was not just me. Her passive-aggressive behavior was directed at most, if not all of the residents, and we swapped stories, each one more absurd than the one before it. We complained to the administration and were told that there was nothing they could do. She had tenure. This was my first taste of bureaucracy at its finest. Once again, it would not be my last.

It was not just the anti-nurse. Before I would see patients on morning rounds, I would check their charts for vital signs. On more than one occasion, there would be a normal blood pressure and temperature written on the chart, yet the patient was dead when I went to see them. There were times when lab techs would write on the chart that the patient declined to have their blood drawn. On one occasion, the patient who reportedly refused was comatose. Obviously, there was no way he had refused.

This was life at the VA, where it seemed that everything fell to the house staff due to limited support staff, especially at night. There were no lab techs to draw blood, except in the morning, or orderlies to transport patients. If you wanted something done, you needed to do it yourself, in between taking histories and physical exams and writing orders.

One night, I got an admission who had a fever and a change in mental status. That is an extremely labor-intensive proposition for an intern, because it meant that in addition to doing a history and physical and writing orders, I needed to draw blood, including two sets of blood cultures half an hour apart, transport the blood to the lab each time, do a spinal tap and transport the fluid to the lab, do gram stains in our makeshift residents' lab to look for bacteria, and transport the patient to radiology, their room or wherever else they needed to go. I drew all the fluids I needed to obtain, transported the patient to radiology, and then proceeded to work on the gram stain and attend to other patients who needed attention. I had not received a page from radiology that my patient was finished, so I finally called them to learn that he had been ready to be transported back to his room for 30 minutes. When I arrived at the radiology department, the technician was sitting in the lounge with her feet up, watching TV. She proceeded to tell me, "The next time, do you think you can get here a little faster? I have other things to do." The lack of respect for a physician, even a lowly intern, was striking to me. I would later write in 2019 about how physicians are being devalued,[5] but this was my first experience with it.

It was crazy at the VA, but I learned how to take care of patients and how to deal with adversity. It was almost like a hazing, which resulted in increased bonding with the other residents. The VA taught us more than just how to take care of patients and how to be a better doctor. I also learned how to take care of myself.

It was at the VA that I got my first taste of rheumatology. While seeing patients in the hospital, there were daily attending rounds, where a member of the attending staff would review cases with the house staff. The purpose of these meetings was not for direct patient care; it was strictly for educational purposes. We would present our most difficult or troublesome cases for some form of guidance or further education about the disease at hand. While rounding in the medical intensive care unit at the VA, our attending was Ralph Schumacher, a world-renowned rheumatologist with special expertise in crystal arthritic conditions, such as gout. As we presented a patient with a complicated cardiac history to him, his focus was on joint pain and whether the patient might have gout. When we saw the patient at bedside, he did not listen to the heart. Instead he examined the big toe. It seemed irrelevant, and almost laughable to me, given the acute nature of the patient's cardiac status, but it planted a seed in me that a career in medicine did not have to be about taking care of the sickest patients whose lives hung in the balance.

Over time, I slowly developed more competence and confidence in my abilities. That was made apparent my first night as a second-year resident at Frankford. Frankford was a small community hospital and did not have a large inpatient population, but the patients there tended to be extremely ill. They were a stoic lot who would not arrive in the emergency room unless they were in absolute crisis. They would not come when they had angina with mild chest tightness; they would wait until they were having an actual heart attack with crushing substernal pain, nausea, vomiting, and shortness of breath. I commented, on more than one occasion, that an extremely ill patient who was having a heart attack with severe congestive heart failure, and in need of an emergent intra-aortic balloon pump, often could not get admitted to the ICU because there were already ten patients there who were sicker than them.

With this background, I faced my first overnight call at Frankford as the most senior person in the hospital, with only an intern and a fourth-year medical student for assistance, although attendings were available for questions if one of their patients was ill. They would not be able to help me this night. The problems started when a patient began to decompensate with a possible heart attack, and we addressed his issues hoping we could stabilize him without having to call a code. While we tended to him, another patient actually did code and I needed to sprint to his room, leaving my intern to handle the first patient while I guided her over the phone. I took the medical student with me. While I was running the code, a third patient developed acute chest pain. All I could do was to send my medical student to address that issue. I was running a code and had both my intern and the medical student on separate phones simultaneously keeping me abreast of what was going on with their ill patients, so I could advise them. Somehow, all three patients survived.

I realized that I could do this job, but that was just the nuts and bolts of the job, in other words, knowing how to interpret the EKG, knowing how to run a code, and knowing what medications to give. Residency taught me how to take care of the sickest hospital patients. As I finished my residency, it struck me that I knew how to take care of a patient with a heart attack, septic shock, or pulmonary edema, but I did not know what to do with a patient who had a cold or a sore throat. I knew how to take care *of* sick patients, but I had not yet understood the importance of caring *for* sick patients, at least not at a conscious level. That is not something that is taught in medical school. One learns how to relate to and treat other people from one's own upbringing. It is an innate attribute, but it is something that can also be taught.

This critical lesson was not something I ever really thought much about until it was hammered home to me at a conscious level the year after residency. Post-residency plans for fellowship or a job need to be determined by the middle of the third year of residency. I had not yet decided by that time to pursue rheumatology, so prior to starting my rheumatology fellowship, I spent a year supervising the ambulatory clinic at MCP. It was there that I met Frank.[6] He was a 25-year-old, gay, African-American male with AIDS, which was still a relatively new diagnosis at the time. Physicians had significant concerns at the time regarding how it was transmitted, and there were no good treatments available. Frank's care was left to me. Frank was quiet, very scared, and quite appreciative of the care that he received. I liked him, but he was one of many patients, and I had no special bond with him. I knew he would not do well in the long run, and I knew

I could not prevent his death. Nonetheless, I did what I could for him. I tended to his needs, answered his phone calls, brought him in to the clinic when he needed to be seen, and listened to him.

I felt some sadness when he finally died, but did not give it too much thought, until I received a note from my nurse in the clinic. She was not one for sentiment, yet she wrote the following:

> Oddly enough I'm not very good at expressing my feelings in writing, but I want to thank you for your care and concerns for Frank and for me. If ever you wonder if it's all worth it or if you make a difference in a patient's life, just remember Frank. You gave him respect, consideration, and self-esteem as well as a feeling of security. He had "his doctor" to turn to when ill or scared. I'm proud to know you and work for you.
>
> —Love, Nel

Nel inherently understood there was much more to medicine than simply knowing how to diagnose and treat disease. This was my first conscious lesson on the importance of humanity in health care. There would be many more.

As noted, I did not decide to pursue a fellowship in rheumatology immediately after residency. People often ask me why I ultimately chose rheumatology. At the time I finally made my decision, the true reasons were unknown to me. I simply told people that I liked the science of rheumatology. I now know that rheumatology was the perfect specialty for me as it correlates well with my personality.

First, I love to solve puzzles of all kinds. Rheumatology is not clear-cut, and I often find myself trying to figure out what is going on physiologically and how to solve the problem, much like a Rubik's Cube. Second, rheumatologic problems are rarely acute. I function much better when I have time to think about things and process them over and over. I would not do well in a specialty where split-second decisions need to be made. That eliminated subspecialties with acutely ill patients such as cardiology, pulmonary, emergency medicine, and surgery. Third, I admittedly like the lifestyle that rheumatology has afforded me. I have almost never been called into the hospital after hours for an acutely ill patient, which has enabled me to have a life outside of medicine. In retrospect, however, the most important factor is that I have been able to follow patients over time and get to know them as individuals. My patients have shared their lives with me, and I have been able to help them, even when I cannot cure their arthritis. Rheumatology is a very "human" subspecialty. That aspect has been especially attractive and incredibly rewarding to me over the years.

As an example, I met "PR" when she was a 25-year-old single woman, working independently. I diagnosed her with lupus. Lupus is an autoimmune disease where the immune system loses the ability to distinguish what is self from what is foreign. The immune system can attack different parts of the body as though they were foreign, most notably the joints, the kidneys, the skin, the central nervous system, and the lining tissue of various organs. It can range from a minor nuisance to a life-threatening illness.

I was able to share PR's ups and downs for more than 25 years. Shortly after I met her, she told me about her new boyfriend, who then became her fiancé, and later her husband. We rejoiced when she became pregnant with her first child and then her second. We despaired when her disease got worse, and she had to stop working. For a quarter of a century, PR made me a part of her life, sharing her joys and sorrows, and opening herself up to me.

I also had a close relationship with another patient to the extent that he honored me by asking me if I would be the executor of his estate once he passed away. I declined, but the idea that he had thought enough of me to have even asked me over his own family members left a lasting impression. The value of these kinds of relationships with patients cannot be quantified.

One of my favorite stories involves my patient "BL," whom I diagnosed with rheumatoid arthritis in 1996. She delivered her second son in 1998 and did well at first, but her arthritis began to worsen after delivery. She wanted to have a third child, but debated the wisdom of doing so. We had numerous lengthy discussions about the pros and cons of her having a third child, and the different pathways we could take to manage her arthritis depending on what she decided. I advised her that if she truly wanted to have a third child, she should not let her illness prevent her from proceeding. Her daughter is now 21 years old and to this day, BL gives me credit for her having that child. Her gratitude has been unending since then. Her arthritis remains well controlled, and the knowledge that I have made a positive difference in her life is priceless. When it comes down to it, all you can really ask for in medicine is the chance to have a positive impact on someone else's life.

This is the aspect of medicine that I especially love. It is what medicine should be all about. It is what sustains me as I deal with the bureaucratic nonsense. Slowly but inexorably, the humanity of health care and the patient-physician relationship are being destroyed by various forms of bureaucracy, but more about that later.

As I finished my year in the clinic, I was eager to start my fellowship at Thomas Jefferson University Hospital. I was especially excited as the chief of rheumatology was going to be giving grand rounds at MCP just before I completed residency. I was filled with pride as I knew my colleagues would be able to see firsthand the leader of my new fellowship program.

Alas, the lecture was one of the worst I had ever heard, and I began to have concerns. These were amplified when, a month later, he gave grand rounds at Jefferson and the chief of medicine thanked him for "spending an hour covering a topic that could have been covered in ten minutes." What had I gotten myself into? Fortunately, the chief of rheumatology, although not a good lecturer, was a good teacher, and I had ample opportunity to learn about the different forms of arthritis and musculoskeletal conditions.

During fellowship, I once again had the opportunity to learn a valuable life lesson about the human component in health care, this time involving my patient "PA," an 18-year-old African-American female with lupus.

At the time, I was very active in Variety Club, a charity for children with various disabilities. I had grown up with Variety Club as my parents were active members. As a teenager, I had attended their annual telethon every year. I worked for several years as a runner for various celebrities, getting them food or coffee or carrying their suitcases or whatever. As I got older and into my mid-twenties, I worked my way up to be one of the leaders of Young Variety, a subgroup of Variety consisting of young professionals. One of my projects there was organizing and coordinating a celebrity bowlathon, which took place on a Sunday afternoon in Willow Grove, a suburb of Philadelphia, about an hour or so from the hospital.

It was in the midst of this event that I got the phone call from the emergency room that PA was there with pericarditis, an inflammation of the lining of the heart, which is not uncommon in lupus. She was going to be admitted to the hospital. I told the ER doctor that I would be in to see her the next day and provided instructions about how to treat her in the meantime. I returned to my responsibilities at the bowling alley as we were in the middle of the fundraiser. Then came the phone call from my attending, who informed me that I must go to the ER right then and there to see the patient. I explained that I was in the middle of a charity event, and that I had already given instructions to the ER doctor. There was not much that was going to change by my going there in person. He would not relent and explained to me that she was my patient, I was her doctor, and that being a doctor meant that I needed to show my face and see the patient, even if it would not change the nature of the treatment she would receive. It would be reassuring to the patient to see me in person and I was obligated to go. I grumbled and resisted, but I left the charity event in the hands of my partner and drove for an hour to the hospital. When I got there, everything was in order. PA was quite frightened and was indeed glad to see me. I was correct that my being there in person did not change her management one iota. However, I learned that taking care of patients is about more than just devising treatment plans over the phone. My mere presence helped to calm her and ease her suffering. It was an important lesson for me to learn and one that stayed with me. Reassurance, demonstrating concern for the patient, and engaging them are all an important part of the therapeutic process. My attending's insistence that I drop what I was doing to go to her was very unpopular with me at the time, but it made me a better doctor in the long run.

I also learned lessons about humility as a fellow. Mr. Johnson was a 34-year-old African-American male who also had lupus, and his case was complicated by sepsis, which occurs when an infection reaches the bloodstream. Some immunosuppressive drugs used to treat lupus can increase the risk of infection. He became very ill fairly quickly, lapsed into a coma, and was transferred to the intensive care unit. Our team rounded on him every day at first, but there was little change. His lupus was not the main issue so there was a very limited role for rheumatology in his care. Every day when we saw him, he remained in a coma. With there being little for us to do, we began to round on him every other day, and then twice a week and then weekly. He remained in a coma for more than six weeks. When January rolled around, we had a new attending take over the service. It was the same attending who had insisted that I see my patient in the ER. I presented the case of Mr. Johnson to him, and he insisted on seeing him immediately. I explained that Mr. Johnson had not changed in weeks and was still in a coma as of the day before, but we made our way to the intensive care unit to see him anyway. When we got there, Mr. Johnson was awake and alert, sitting up in bed reading the newspaper. He earned the nickname "Magic" Johnson that day. He ultimately recovered and left the hospital. I learned not to be so cocksure of myself, and that there are things in medicine that are simply beyond our realm of understanding. Magic Johnson's abrupt recovery after more than six weeks in a coma was one of them.

There were humorous stories as well. As part of my fellowship, I had the opportunity to see patients with Phillip Marone, who was a well-known orthopedist and the Phillies team physician at the time. One day, an elderly man walked in using a golf club as a cane. He was complaining of back pain. Phil asked him if he had been playing a lot of golf, and the man nodded yes. Phil then asked him, "Why do you insist on playing golf and then coming in to see me, complaining of back pain?" The patient responded, "Well I would rather play golf and come to see you, than not play golf and have to go see a psychiatrist."

People have passions, and sometimes their mental health takes precedence over their physical pain. Patients are more than just the illness they present with. They are more than "the gall bladder in room 301." Later in my career, I had a patient with osteoporosis, which made her susceptible to fractures. She absolutely refused to give up horseback riding, even after breaking multiple bones in a fall. A good physician recognizes and understands their patient's interests. I often would put notes in a patient's chart about their passion, a new grandchild, or an upcoming vacation, so that I would remember to ask them about it at their follow-up visits. Their faces would light up when I did so. Patients need to be treated as people, not as numbers.

I was to complete my fellowship in June of 1989, and it was time to look for a real job. The job search was not productive. I didn't want to leave the Philadelphia area, but there simply were not any rheumatology openings there. I had the opportunity to buy a practice in Delaware, but I had zero confidence in my business acumen. I knew that I lacked the ability to do what was necessary in terms of hiring staff, advertising, and generally managing my own practice. Ultimately, I took a job in the primary care department at my alma mater, MCP. Although I would be spending most of my time doing primary care there, I was assured that any rheumatology cases in the department would be referred to me, rather than the rheumatology division. Location was important, and I was in a familiar academic institution, with the opportunity to teach house staff. I also did not have to deal with any of the headaches associated with managing a practice. I therefore accepted the position in 1989. I was not doing full-time rheumatology, but otherwise I was content for the time being, when my life turned on one of those dimes.

I had broken up with my long-standing girlfriend in September of 1989. Bachelorhood lasted about eight months for me, until my sister-in-law told me she wanted me to meet one of her fellow teachers at her religious school. She arranged a blind date and I met my future wife, Suzan, at my brother's house in May of 1990. I was not initially impressed. We had Chinese food and played Pictionary. My wife has many wonderful features but artistry is not one of them. There was no magical spark that night. There was simply nothing special about the date, but for reasons that remain unknown to me even today, when I walked her to her car, I blurted out, "I would like to see you again, without them."

We began to date. Despite our fledgling romance, she took a job away from me at a dinner theater in Cape May that summer, with the idea that if our relationship was meant to be, it would happen. I visited her there and soon we were an exclusive item, albeit at a distance. I learned a lot from her as we grew closer. I had never really processed how to deal with conflict, and when we had our first fight, I assumed our relationship was over. She was incredulous at that idea and taught me instead how to deal with conflict. She also greatly helped me to become more assertive, as this was never one of my strong suits. The skills that I learned from her would serve me well in the years to come. We were engaged in February 1991, with plans for a November wedding.

In October of 1991, a month before the wedding, my life took another acute detour. I was attending the annual Pemberton lecture at the College of Physicians in Philadelphia. This special lecture in memory of rheumatology pioneer Ralph Pemberton was held every year and attracted nationally known speakers as well as rheumatologists from throughout the city. During the reception after the lecture, while walking from one area to another, I happened to pass one of my rheumatology colleagues speaking to another person whom I did not know. I overheard that this other person was looking for a new rheumatologist for his practice. I later asked my colleague whom he had been talking to, and he told me it was Robert Gatter, who had an opening for his rheumatology practice in Willow Grove. I subsequently approached Bob, introduced myself, and was able to arrange an interview, which was conducted in early November, two and a half weeks before my wedding. I was fortunate to be offered the job and started in private practice there in June of 1992. The experiences in that practice greatly shaped my subsequent thinking about health care and the injustices and bureaucracy that influence the care that patients receive. Had I remained in my prior practice as a primary care hospital employee, I do not think these issues would have been so much in my face, or caused me to react so strongly. I often reflect that if I had walked by ten seconds earlier or ten seconds later, I would not have overheard that Bob was looking for a new associate. My whole world completely changed because I happened to walk by at the exact moment that I did.

Chapter 2

Legal

From 1992 to 1999, life was quiet, for the most part. I grew into the rhythms of private practice, gaining more experience in taking care of rheumatology outpatients and learning how to manage my time, both in and out of the office. My wife and I had our first child, Dana, in 1993 and our second one, Melanie, in 1995. I began my buy-in to the practice in 1994 and became a full-fledged partner in 1998.

Life was going quite swimmingly as of December 1999, when my life again pivoted dramatically, this time in a negative direction. People do not usually knock at your door at 8:30 on a Sunday evening, and if they do, it is not usually an indication that something good is about to happen. I was soon to learn that there was a very good reason for concern. A crash course in medical malpractice and our legal system was headed my way. My young daughters were already in bed when I answered the door. The man there asked if I was Dr. Mark Lopatin. When I answered yes, he handed me the papers that would start my life on a different trajectory. I was being served with papers alleging malpractice on my part.

It is bad enough to be named in a lawsuit, but the actual accusations are horrifying. Phrases like "wanton disregard," "gross negligence," and "reckless endangerment" littered the paper. The words "sheer terror" do not do justice to the emotions I felt that evening. How could someone possibly accuse me of deliberately harming a patient, with a blatant disregard for their well-being? That was the exact antithesis of how I viewed myself as a doctor. I later learned that this is boilerplate language designed to elicit the exact emotion that it elicited in me: fear! Someone who is afraid is more likely to surrender. I was already 42 years old, but still quite inexperienced and quite unsophisticated. I had no knowledge of this sort of thing. A million thoughts regarding my self-worth and my future ran through my brain. I was terrified of what would happen.

I barely slept that night. I could not wait to get to the office the next morning to read the chart and see what I might have done wrong and why these accusations were being made. This was before computerized patient charts, so I spent that Sunday night in agony awaiting my fate. I was not sure that life would ever be the same again. I was right, but I did not realize then that things would actually get worse for me a few years later.

The case involved a patient, "CK," whom I saw for the first time in June 1997. She wrote on our initial intake form that she was seeing me for "aches, pains, and stiffness in her feet, hands, legs, and arms, along with fatigue." As part of the routine questioning at her initial visit, I asked if she suffered from headaches. She answered no. The workup for her muscle and joint pain was unrevealing and I diagnosed her with fibromyalgia. Her primary care physician had started her on medication just prior to her initial visit with me, so I made no changes to her regimen at that time. At her follow-up visit with me two weeks later, she was much better. There was not much change in her condition over the next few months and there was not much for me to do, given her level of improvement. She was doing well as of February 1998, when she saw me for the final time. I did not give her a second thought until December 1999 when I was served with the papers.

The malpractice complaint alleged that I was negligent for failing to diagnose a meningioma, a type of brain tumor whose principal manifestation is headache. Although headache is the cardinal symptom of a meningioma, CK had never reported a headache to me. Furthermore, the diagnosis of a meningioma is outside the realm of expertise of a rheumatologist. Essentially, I was sued for failure to diagnose an illness outside my area of expertise, in a patient who never mentioned the critical symptom of that illness, despite my specifically asking if she had this symptom.

I was somewhat reassured once I had reviewed her chart and had a chance to talk with my lawyer. I was still quite upset, but I recognized this was a meritless lawsuit. My lawyer agreed and said there was no case against me.

However, for whatever reason, the plaintiff's attorney refused to drop the case. One of the requirements for a medical malpractice lawsuit to proceed is that the plaintiff's attorney must obtain expert testimony critical of the defendant's actions. The plaintiff's attorney was unable to do so for two and a half years, yet he refused to relent. Ultimately, my attorney literally forced him to dismiss the case by filing a petition for contempt on this basis. The lawsuit was finally dropped in May of 2002, more than four years after I had last seen her, with no payment being made to her by my malpractice insurer on my behalf.

The case aroused my anger, however. The fact that this suit was filed and allowed to linger for two and a half years despite zero evidence of any wrongdoing on my part was a travesty and a condemnation of our legal system. Since then, I have had plaintiffs' attorneys tell me on more than one occasion that lawyers do not file frivolous lawsuits. This is simply not true as evidenced by this case. My medical legal education had started, and although it was very upsetting, I was able to manage the stress of this lawsuit for the most part.

I did not realize it at the time I was served with papers for this lawsuit, but things were about to get much worse. My medical legal education was destined to become much more extensive. This time my life did not just turn on a dime. It nearly careened off the road.

In the midst of the nonsense with this first case, there was another legal storm brewing. If the first case was analogous to a tropical storm, this was a hurricane, and it hit land only a few months after I was named in the first suit. Thus, I was dealing with two lawsuits at the same time. This second lawsuit posed a much greater threat to me.

The second case involved a patient, "RF," whom I actually saw for the first time in January 1997, before I had even met CK. I recognized RF would be a difficult patient from the first time I met her. She was a nurse, with a somewhat sullen demeanor and a notebook full of records. She presented with a history of joint and muscle pain present for ten years prior to her initial visit with me. She also answered yes to multiple symptoms affecting multiple body systems. She struck me as a demanding Type A patient with multiple chronic complaints, and I recognized it would be difficult to address all of them to her satisfaction.

I diagnosed RF with fibromyalgia and prescribed various medications to address her condition. Things went reasonably well for the next year, and we established what I considered to be a semblance of rapport. I spent extra time at each visit answering her many questions, and I began to feel that she trusted me.

In February of 1998, she developed dizziness and decreased hearing for which she saw an otorhinolaryngologist (ear, nose, and throat physician). He made a presumptive diagnosis of autoimmune sensorineural hearing loss (AISNHL). He started her on 60 mg of prednisone per day on March 20 and referred her to another rheumatologist, Dr. H. She was no longer my patient. Dr. H switched her to another steroid, Medrol, at a comparable dose on March 27.

Prednisone and Medrol are corticosteroids, which are powerful anti-inflammatory agents. They are distinct from the anabolic steroids that athletes sometimes use. Sixty milligrams of prednisone is a relatively high dose, but doses like this are routinely used when there is a significant threat to the body such as loss of hearing as occurred in this case. One of the most important things physicians think about when we start a patient on a steroid is how we will get them off of it. They are not medications that can be stopped abruptly. They must be tapered, but we walk a fine line when we do so. If we taper them too slowly, the patient risks potential side effects from the medication. If we taper them too rapidly, the underlying illness can wreak havoc.

RF called me on April 13, desperate to be seen immediately. She had learned that Dr. H had not accepted her insurance and she needed help. I fitted her into my schedule on an emergency basis that day, and once again she became my patient. She complained of multiple severe joint and muscle pains at that visit, although that was nothing new for her. She had been on steroids for only three weeks by then. Her hearing and dizziness had improved, but she was worried that the steroids were causing side effects. I wanted to lower the steroids, but was concerned about what would happen to her hearing if I decreased the dosage.

Nonetheless, RF felt strongly that the steroids were increasing her aches and pains, and I cautiously began to taper them, despite the improvement in her hearing since she had started on them. By May 30, I had tapered her Medrol dosage fairly rapidly down to 20 mg per day. On June 2, she requested another emergency visit, complaining of severe knee pain. Given that the pain was localized to one knee, which was unusual for her, I ordered an MRI to look for any structural damage.

I saw RF again the following week, while the MRI results were still pending. Her hearing had not worsened with the steroid taper, and I felt it was safe to continue tapering her steroids. I decreased her dosage to 16 mg per day, with instructions to reduce it further to 12 mg per day in two weeks.

On June 16, I finally received the results of her MRI. It revealed avascular necrosis (AVN) in her knee. Avascular necrosis is a condition where a bone loses its blood supply, essentially causing something analogous to a heart attack in the bone, resulting in significant pain. It is a known side effect of steroid use, although not a common one. It usually occurs with more prolonged use of steroids than had occurred in this case.

Two days later, I learned that she was seeing an orthopedic surgeon with complaints of multiple joint pains. He ordered further MRIs that demonstrated widespread avascular necrosis involving both knees, both shoulders, both ankles, and both hips. Although AVN is a known side effect of steroids, this type of widespread AVN was distinctly unusual. In view of this, RF then began to question whether her original diagnosis of AISNHL had been accurate and whether she should have been started on steroids in the first place.

At this point, I suspected there would be a lawsuit, but I did not realize that I was at risk. After all, I was the one RF had called when she was in trouble. I was the one who had brought her in on two separate occasions for emergency visits on the same day she had called. I was the one who had rapidly tapered her off the steroids. I was the one who had ordered the MRI that led to the correct diagnosis. My one mistake, however, was being one of her treating physicians. That alone put me at risk, regardless of any actions I had taken on her case.

RF's dose of Medrol was down to 2 mg per day by July, and I actually had to increase her dosage for a short time because of adrenal insufficiency. Sometimes when a patient's steroids are tapered too rapidly, their adrenal glands may not function properly. If that happens, the dose has to be increased again, and then tapered more slowly. By August, she was off steroids completely, only five months after having started them for an autoimmune condition that threatened her hearing. As a point of comparison, there is a condition in rheumatology, temporal arteritis, which threatens another sense organ, the eye. In that condition, inflammation of the artery that provides blood supply to the eye can cause blindness. Temporal arteritis is usually treated with steroids for a year or more, so I considered a five-month taper of steroids without relapse of hearing loss to be a success.

Over the next year, RF saw several orthopedic surgeons and other otorhinolaryngologists, and had several joint surgeries. She now required opioids to manage her pain. She was seeing a new internist for this as her prior internist had discharged her from his practice. Her fibromyalgia became a secondary issue, and my role in her care diminished once she was off the steroids. However, I still saw her on a fairly regular basis thereafter.

In March 1999, I received a request for her medical records. When I asked her why, she informed me that she was suing the otorhinolaryngologist who'd made the original diagnosis of AISNHL, and that her lawyer wanted to learn more about her fibromyalgia. She said nothing about suing me.

In August of the same year, she sent me a nice note thanking me for helping her out with some forms, and for expediting an earlier appointment with an orthopedic surgeon. She gave no hint of any displeasure with my care, and routinely scheduled follow-up appointments. In fact, she continued to see me until December 1999.

Then the roof caved in Dr. H, the other rheumatologist, called me in February 2000, asking me why he'd been named in her lawsuit, since he had only seen her once. This was only two months after the first lawsuit against me had been filed. Dr. H informed me that I also had been named in the lawsuit, although this time, I was never actually served with papers. Once again, it was a gut punch, creating an instant panic that made it difficult to function the rest of that day. I had no idea why I had been named in her lawsuit. I had done nothing wrong.

I later learned that I was being charged with not tapering RF's steroids quickly enough, and for not recognizing her avascular necrosis sooner. I was floored by this accusation, especially since the steroids had in fact been tapered quite rapidly, and as noted, perhaps a little too rapidly as evidenced by her adrenal insufficiency in July! She was also questioning if she even had AISNHL and whether she should have been placed on steroids in the first place.

Assessing the case in hindsight, her accusations against me did not have merit. First, it should be noted that I was not the physician who made the diagnosis of AISNHL. Similar to the first case, this is a diagnosis outside the realm of rheumatology and I had to rely on the otorhinolaryngologist for the accuracy of this diagnosis. Having said that, I did not routinely accept the diagnosis based on the patient's report. I specifically spoke with the otorhinolaryngologist to confirm the diagnosis. The otorhinolaryngologist informed me that RF could lose her hearing completely if not treated with steroids. Simply stopping the steroids or tapering them too fast posed a threat to her hearing.

Thus, her argument that I should have tapered her steroids more rapidly was not justified. Weighing all of the variables, I recognized that I had to walk a tightrope. If she truly had experienced AVN as a result of steroid use, tapering them too slowly could result in further damage, but RF could have suffered deafness or adrenal insufficiency if I tapered the steroids too quickly. The patient did indeed suffer adrenal insufficiency at the tail end of her taper, as noted, but I did successfully wean her off the steroids in only five months, with no recurrence of dizziness or hearing loss.

As for recognizing AVN more quickly, this was a patient who had been having widespread joint and muscle pains for more than ten years. There was no reason to suspect that her complaints of multiple joint pains in the spring of 1998 represented a different entity. When she did complain of a localized joint pain in early June that I deemed to be different, I immediately ordered an MRI and made the diagnosis. Multifocal AVN is a very rare entity and would not routinely be suspected, especially in a patient with long-standing pain.

She also alleged that her problems started on April 13, which was the day I saw her on an emergency basis. It would be remarkably unusual for a patient to develop multifocal AVN so soon after starting steroids.

Of course, at the time I learned of the lawsuit against me, I immediately scoured RF's chart, looking for errors I might have made, but I couldn't find anything I would have done differently. My attorney reviewed the chart, and told me that my documentation was excellent, that I'd done nothing wrong, and that my case was strong for all of the reasons listed above. He then told me to throw those reasons out the window, as they would not likely influence the jury. He explained that I was now at the mercy of our legal system, and that a jury might not see things my way, particularly given RF's extensive medical problems. It was my first experience with a situation where the facts did not matter. It would not be the last, and "The Facts Did Not Matter" would become the title of an article I wrote years later about another case.[7]

There were other problems as well. The defendant otorhinolaryngologist practiced in Philadelphia, a city notorious for big jury awards. Therefore, it was considered to be a favorable venue for plaintiffs' attorneys, compared with suburban counties, where I provided RF's care. Because of that, the plaintiff's attorney had the case tried in Philadelphia, which would prove to be a major factor in the resolution of this lawsuit. Venue has been a huge issue over the years in the debate for medical malpractice reform, and this case provided a prime example of why venue remains a critical factor, even today, in the medical malpractice landscape.

On a separate note, I was the guy with the "deep pockets" in the case. I had twice as much insurance coverage as the otorhinolaryngologist, and due to a slip-up, Dr. H, the other rheumatologist, had no insurance at all. He was therefore dismissed from the case. This meant that a large award to the plaintiff would affect me the most. According to the doctrine of joint and several liability present at the time, all defendants are equally responsible for the award in a lawsuit, regardless of their level of responsibility for causing the injuries. Thus, even if the otorhinolaryngologist was deemed to be 99% responsible for the outcome and I was felt to be 1% responsible, we each would be equally responsible for paying damages to the patient. Furthermore, I would be equally responsible for any judgment that exceeded the insurance coverage regardless of my level of responsibility. That meant that unless a jury exonerated me 100%, I would be on the hook for 50% of the damages awarded to the plaintiff, and if the other defendant could not pay, I would be 100% responsible. That was a frightening proposition to me. Could I lose my home and personal assets? Could I lose everything I had worked for over the years?

My deposition went well, but the trial judge was pushing for a settlement, rather than a court case. Just before the scheduled trial, my attorney and I discussed potential courses of action. He explained again that I had done nothing wrong, and that my care and documentation were appropriate. He noted that the case against me had no merit based on the facts of the case. However, he also informed me again that a jury in Philadelphia would more likely reach a decision based on the emotional impact of the plaintiff's alleged injuries rather than the medical facts. He stated that Philadelphia juries tend to be more sympathetic to plaintiffs and that my chart notes, even though they were very well documented, would likely not play much of a role in the jury's decision-making. I found that information to be quite disheartening. Furthermore, because the plaintiff had significant joint problems, the potential of a high judgment in favor of the plaintiff was quite realistic. Even though I felt strongly that I had provided proper care, I now had significant concerns about proceeding to trial given the potential risks that my attorney had pointed out. I was not so sure I was willing to rely on a Philadelphia jury to get this right, given what my attorney had described. There was simply too much to lose.

Given the combined factors of a possible high monetary award, the threat to my personal assets, and most importantly the change in venue to Philadelphia, my attorney maintained that the risks of going to trial outweighed the benefits. He noted that if I went to trial, I might win, but if I lost, I would risk a verdict that could potentially exceed my coverage. If I settled the case, however, it would be over, with a payment being made by my malpractice carrier, and no threat to my personal assets. He advised me to settle the case despite his acknowledgment that no malpractice had been committed. He assured me that whether I settled or not, the sun would continue to rise each day.

The stress level was enormous. After much soul-searching, and weighing the potential risks and benefits, I finally decided to follow my attorney's recommendation, even though I knew in my heart that I had done nothing wrong. I was naive and scared, and settling would make this go away. I would not have made that same decision today. The case was resolved in April of 2002. The big question at the time then became how I could live with that decision, feeling that I had surrendered, even though I had met the standard of care. How could

I look my kids in the eye when I've always told them to fight for what's right? My anguish was palpable in the days to come, especially to Suzan, who saw my pain every day.

The kicker in all of this was that a number of years later, RF got a job working as a nurse in my primary hospital. I would see her on the floors walking rapidly without a cane or even a limp, and my blood would boil. I never said a word to her or approached her in any way, but this only served to increase my pain and anger with regard to what I had endured.

After I settled, my lawyer was right in that the sun did continue to rise each day. However, I was too outraged to appreciate it. I felt violated and became suspicious, if not a little paranoid. Who else would sue me now, I wondered? What if another patient had an unexpected adverse effect from a medication I prescribed? What if a patient had an unfortunate outcome despite proper care? How could I continue to care for patients with these thoughts hanging over my head? My patients came to me for help. I now saw them as potential adversaries. My rage at plaintiffs' lawyers and the legal system went on unabated. The questions then became how I was going to deal with this emotionally and how I was going to be able to continue to practice.

Both of these cases demonstrated a broken legal system in need of repair. Patients have every right to be made as whole as possible when malpractice occurs, but there is tremendous damage done to a physician when they are sued. This was readily illustrated to me when I spoke with one of my colleagues about a lawsuit that he had won. He said to me, "Tell me exactly what I have won. I have spent weeks out of the office and countless hours defending this. I have had an inordinate amount of stress over this, with the end result being that I am told that I have not done anything wrong. That is not winning."

His words rang true and after the wringer that I had been through, I could easily relate to them and to his experience. His point was that a physician loses a lawsuit 100% of the time, regardless of the final verdict.

I had survived the lawsuits, but at what cost? There was so much poison inside me, and no matter how much I tried to vomit it out by venting repeatedly, I could not get rid of it. Suzan was truly a trooper. Her patience was remarkable as I ranted and raved incessantly about how unfair it all was, but this was nothing compared to the support she would give me a few years later, when my entire career was at stake.

Chapter 3

Tort Reform

I needed an outlet for my anger, other than my wife. Ultimately, I required professional counseling to help me cope with the venom inside of me. I began to
pay attention to what was going on around me with regard to the malpractice crisis much like how when you are shopping for a new car, you notice every vehicle
on the road. This process was an evolution for me, taking several years.

For the first time in my life, I began to explore the political realm. I joined
the Politically Active Physicians Association (PAPA), a grassroots organization
formed in July 2002, shortly after my lawsuit had been settled. Their main objective was reform of the medical malpractice situation.[8]

The malpractice crisis was a hot topic in the early 2000s, with multiple com-
mentaries appearing in newspapers and magazines, including *Time* in June 2003
and *Newsweek* in December 2003. I wrote an article about what I had experienced, which was published in *Medical Economics* in June 2004.[9] I hoped that it
would help others in the same situation, but realistically it was more for therapeutic purposes, as it provided me with yet another opportunity to vent. I also
began to write "letters to the editor" to various newspapers regarding malpractice issues. I had never done that before.

One of my first letters was written in 2004, when the drug Vioxx was taken
off the market. Nonsteroidal anti-inflammatory drugs (NSAIDs) such as Motrin
and Naproxen are effective medications for reducing arthritic pain and inflammation, but one of their main side effects is upset stomach, along with increased
risk of stomach ulcers. That is why they should always be taken with food. Vioxx
was a new type of NSAID that worked by a different mechanism, resulting in a
lower risk of gastrointestinal upset and ulcer. Approved in 1999, it was a very
effective drug; however, it began to emerge that patients taking the drug had an

increased risk of cardiac events. Merck, the pharmaceutical company that made the drug, was soon inundated with lawsuits on this basis. The problem with these lawsuits was that although there was a higher incidence of cardiac events in a population of patients taking Vioxx compared to a population of patients not taking it, there was no way to know if Vioxx played a role in an individual patient who had sustained a cardiac event. This did not stop the lawyers from placing newspaper ads encouraging patients to participate in lawsuits if they had taken the drug. The result was that Merck voluntarily took the drug off the market in September of 2004. It was not the Food and Drug Administration (FDA) who removed the drug.

It certainly is debatable whether or not this drug should have remained on the market, given this risk. I would not have objected to its removal if the FDA had decided that the risks exceeded the benefits, but I was quite upset that the removal was determined based on the threat of legal action.

I therefore wrote the following letter to the editor, which was published in both the *Philadelphia Inquirer* and our local newspaper:

> With all the talk of tort reform, it is important to realize that lawsuit abuse extends beyond the current malpractice crisis. I am referring to the recall of Vioxx. A recent study showed a 2× greater risk of cardiac events in patients taking Vioxx compared to those taking placebo. This data must be put in perspective. The risk of a cardiac event increased from 3/4 of an event per 100 patient-years in the placebo group to 1 1/2 events per 100 patient-years in the Vioxx group. Thus, the risk increased by less than one cardiac event for every 100 patients taking the drug for a year. Furthermore, there were an equal number of deaths in each group.
>
> So why did Merck recall the drug? I believe that the threat of legal action was more than Merck could bear financially. What is more troubling, however, is that each patient no longer has the option to decide if the added risk is worth it. Legal pressure has compromised our right to choose. Many of my patients feel worse without the drug and are willing to accept the added cardiac risks in order to have an improved quality of life. Now, they don't have a choice!

Finally, I am appalled by newspaper ads from law firms seeking clients. My patients have received "cold calls" from lawyers encouraging them to sue. One patient was asked, "How do you know you weren't hurt by the drug?" This type of ambulance chasing is reprehensible. When lawyers cause our individual rights to be taken away in the name of "helping the public," we must object strenuously! It is incumbent upon all of us to act against this form of legalized terrorism.

The letter was written only three years after the attacks on September 11. My use of the words "legalized terrorism" was indicative of how passionate I felt about this issue and how much the lawsuits had affected me.

Throughout this time, I was beginning to grasp the scope of the problem as I realized that I was not alone with regard to the issue of medical malpractice lawsuits. There have been numerous studies citing the frequency of such lawsuits, including one I did myself. One such study in the *New England Journal of Medicine*[10] in 2011 revealed that by the age of 65 years, 75% of physicians in low-risk specialties and 99% of those in high-risk specialties were projected to face a malpractice claim. Thirty-six percent of physicians in low-risk specialties and 88% in high-risk specialties were projected to face their first claim by the age of 45. In internal medicine and its subspecialties, roughly 55% of physicians were projected to face a malpractice lawsuit by the age of 45. This number goes up to 80% for physicians in surgical specialties (including general surgery) and 74% for physicians in obstetrics and gynecology. Eighty-nine percent of physicians in internal medicine and its specialties can expect to be sued by the age of 65 years. These numbers are stunning.

Learning that I was not alone helped some, as one of the most stressful aspects of a lawsuit is the sense of isolation—the feeling that you are the only one to ever go through it. When you are sued, you are not supposed to talk with anyone else as anything you say could conceivably be used against you. The result is that you suffer in silence, unable to share the pain or receive comfort from other physicians. I was not even allowed to discuss the details with my partners, who only knew that I was being sued.

Getting sued for malpractice strikes us at our core as physicians. When we go to a party and meet a new person, we begin to learn who they are. We draw immediate conclusions regarding gender and approximate age, based on their appearance. We typically ask if they are married or if they have kids. One of the first questions asked is what they do for a living. Our job, or profession, is a part of the basic nucleus of how we view ourselves, so a malpractice suit attacks our core identity as a physician.

A few years after navigating this ordeal, I returned from a vacation to see a notice that there were important papers waiting for me at the post office. It was a Saturday afternoon and I would have to wait until Monday to learn what this was about. Nonetheless, I somehow knew instantly that I was about to be sued and I was filled with dread for the rest of the weekend. Once you have gone through a lawsuit, there is a never-ending fear that you will have to experience it again. Any request for records received in the office from an attorney would fill me with panic until I learned that the attorney was not after me. Typically it was for a disability case or an injury at work, and I was able to breathe again once I realized I was not at risk.

Monday finally came and I was apprehensive as I went to the post office. I opened the letter and learned that, yes, I was being sued, but in this case it was for a fender bender a year earlier. I was absolutely elated because I was not being sued for malpractice. Being a driver is not part of my identity—being a doctor is. Getting sued for a car accident was a hassle, but it did not attack my identity or my sense of self-worth.

Malpractice lawsuits can have a tremendous effect on the psyche of a physician. A study of more than 25,000 physicians published in the *Journal of the American College of Surgery* stated that "recent malpractice suits were strongly related to burnout, depression, and recent thoughts of suicide among surgeons."[11]

Medical Malpractice Stress Syndrome (MMSS), a condition similar to PTSD, is a well-described entity in physicians who have been sued. It consists primarily of symptoms reflecting anxiety and depression. Feelings of self-doubt, worthlessness, and an extreme fear of another event are common.[12] Although I have never been formally diagnosed with MMSS, this description applies to me. In many cases, symptoms can become chronic, affecting sleep, work satisfaction, and long-standing relationships. In one survey of 99 physicians who had a claim completed during the previous year, 80.8% acknowledged having suffered significant emotional distress, regardless of the claim's outcome.[13]

Another study looked at self-reports from 220 physicians who had fought medical liability cases in Cook County, Illinois, from 1977 to 1981.[14] The survey noted that 90% of the doctors suffered significant mental effects from the lawsuits. After the cases ended, half of the physicians stopped offering certain services. Another 50% dropped certain types of patients. However, the most disturbing effect was that 10% of the doctors actually contemplated suicide. It should be noted that these were all circumstances in which the physicians *won* their case. The effects of a lawsuit on a physician can be devastating, affecting the way they practice and the services they provide, thereby also affecting patients.

One of the results of this is defensive medicine. Defensive medicine is defined as providing medical services that are not expected to benefit the patient but are instead undertaken to minimize the risk of a subsequent lawsuit. Defensive medicine can also be "negative," occurring when physicians avoid treating certain types of patients or restrict their practices to avoid procedures or interventions that are perceived as being high-risk. This was described by the Cook County physicians.

When I lecture on the subject of malpractice, I typically start by presenting the case of "DA." He was a 78-year-old male with a history of Parkinson's, hypothyroidism, and coronary artery disease, who called me one night in 2005, seeking advice. The call came at 10:00 p.m. on a cold winter's night. My prior lawsuit experiences from a few years earlier were still fresh in my mind. He had been having bad cold symptoms all day with a dry cough, sore throat, low-grade fever, and fatigue. The most likely diagnosis was a viral infection, and the best treatment for him overnight was bed rest, fluids, and Tylenol at home, but what if it were a bacterial infection, or worse yet, sepsis? These would be much less likely but neither should wait until morning to be addressed. The question in my mind was whether to send him to the emergency room, "just in case." I recognized it would be unpleasant and uncomfortable for him to have to go and would more likely serve me than him. Should I send him to the ER simply to lower my risk of a lawsuit, even if I did not think it would benefit him? I always pose the question to my audience: What would they do in this case?

This case was a prime example of defensive medicine because the patient in question was my father. Therefore, I had no fear of a lawsuit and felt confident making a recommendation based on what I thought was best for him, rather than what would lower my own anxiety level. I advised him to rest, drink fluids, and take Tylenol, and I would reassess him the next morning. He did so and felt much better after a good night's sleep. Problem solved, but what if the patient had not been my father?

Patients often specifically ask me to give them the same recommendations I would give to a family member. It does not always work that way as evidenced by this case. Given the recent lawsuits I had experienced, I doubt I would have given the same advice to one of my patients. I suspect I would have sent them off to the ER, "just in case." This is an example of how defensive medicine is not necessarily in the best interest of the patient.

I have talked about health care being a human endeavor. That also applies to physicians who have fears and anxieties that influence their decision-making just as fears and anxieties affect the decision-making of everyone else in the population. I typically make use of the sleep test when I receive an after-hours call from a patient. As I weigh whether to make a specific recommendation, I ask myself the question, "If I give this particular advice to my patient, will I be able to sleep tonight"? Sometimes that may mean an unnecessary visit to the emergency room for a patient, not just because of my fear of a lawsuit, but typically more often because of a fear of being wrong and someone suffering as a result. I would be lying, however, if I said that the fear of a lawsuit played no role in my day-to-day decision-making or in my documentation.

My point is that the medical malpractice environment is not just a problem for physicians. More importantly, it affects patient care as it influences how physicians treat patients. Defensive medicine results in an overuse of technology with unnecessary lab tests, imaging studies, and procedures. It causes increased referrals to specialists, increased use of the emergency room, overreading of reports, and ultimately decreased access to care. If the emergency room staff is occupied taking care of non-emergent issues, what happens when a patient arrives who does have a legitimate emergency? Will the emergency room have the resources to address the problem urgently? If a specialist has a schedule filled with patients seeing him "just in case," how long does another patient have to wait to see that specialist? Sometimes patients endure increased financial stresses due to the costs of unnecessary testing that is ordered "just in case." Even worse, some patients undergo unnecessary procedures such as biopsies or even surgery, "just in case." It is unfortunate that a litigious environment has resulted in medicine being practiced this way. The end result is this "just in case" mentality, which typically does not benefit patients.

Research shows that defensive medicine is widespread. In a survey of 824 physicians in high-risk specialties, 93% reported practicing defensive medicine.[15] Defensive medicine manifested as "assurance behavior" in 92%, consisting of behaviors such as ordering tests, performing diagnostic procedures, and referring patients for consultation. Forty-three percent of physicians reported using imaging technology in clinically unnecessary circumstances. Forty-two percent of respondents engaged in avoidance behaviors, including eliminating procedures prone to complications, such as trauma surgery, and avoiding patients who had complex medical problems or were perceived as litigious.

Over 76% of physicians in the survey were concerned that malpractice litigation has hurt their ability to provide quality care to patients.[16] Seventy-nine percent said that they had ordered more tests than they would order based solely on professional judgment of what is medically needed. Ninety-one percent noticed other physicians ordering more tests. Furthermore, 74% referred patients to specialists more often than they believed was medically necessary.

The financial costs of defensive medicine and our malpractice system in general are difficult to assess but are felt to be impressive. One study estimated defensive medicine costs to be $46 billion,[17] although its authors acknowledge that the quality of evidence supporting this figure is low.

A subsequent analysis by PricewaterhouseCoopers estimated that approximately 10% of the costs of medical services are attributed to the cost of litigation and defensive medicine.[18] According to the Centers for Medicare and Medicaid Services (CMS), the total annual health costs were $3.8 trillion in 2019.[19] That amounts to a cost of $11,582 per person per year. Ten percent would place the total expenditures related to the malpractice environment at $380 billion per year.

These studies are small potatoes, however, compared to a study done by Jackson Healthcare, a health-care solutions company. They conducted a Gallup poll as well as their own survey in 2009–2010 of over 3,000 physicians to assess the economic costs of defensive medicine. The results were published in an e-book entitled *A Costly Defense: Physicians Sound Off on The High Price of Defensive Medicine in the U.S.*[20]

Their report notes that 72% of physicians in the Gallup poll and 92% in their own survey acknowledged making medical decisions to avoid lawsuits. Furthermore, obstetricians estimated that 38% of all C-sections were performed to avoid litigation. Physicians as a whole estimated that 35% of diagnostic tests, 29% of laboratory tests, 19% of hospitalizations, 14% of prescriptions, and 8% of surgeries were medically unnecessary and defensive in nature. Many physicians described practicing "rule-out medicine" rather than "diagnostic medicine" out of fear that they would miss a diagnosis or be accused of delaying diagnosis. One physician stated that "every word that I write on every form is crafted with the idea that a malpractice attorney will challenge me to defend my practice." It is difficult to practice medicine when you feel you must justify every decision.

This report goes on to say that the annual estimated cost of defensive medicine is in the range of $650–850 billion, or between 26% and 34% of annual health-care costs in the U.S. The authors comment that "in addition to economic costs created by these unnecessary tests, treatments and admissions, defensive medicine exposes patients to risks unrelated to their medical conditions." For example, a physician may undertreat cancer to avoid being sued by the patient for the side effects, or a child may be overexposed to radiation in an effort to "rule out" various diagnoses.

According to the same publication, no physician respondents in the United Kingdom, New Zealand, Canada, or Sweden reported practicing defensive medicine. Likewise, physicians working under contract with the federal government reported practicing significantly less defensive medicine than their private sector peers.[21]

Suffice it to say that the financial costs of litigation are quite high. There was truly a crisis regarding the need for tort reform at the time of my lawsuits. Admittedly, my motivation in advocating for tort reform at the outset was primarily based on my own emotional needs, but there was a dire need for tort reform for more than my personal reasons. Malpractice premiums were sky-rocketing and many physicians responded by either retiring or leaving Pennsylvania on this basis. It was next to impossible to recruit new physicians, unless they had some ties to the area. Patients were losing their physicians. Access to care was diminished further. One example of this was when Abington Memorial Hospital closed its trauma center at the end of 2002 because the doctors staffing the facility could not obtain affordable medical liability insurance.[22] Philadelphia, the venue for my lawsuit, was listed as a judicial hellhole and the American Medical Association (AMA) listed Pennsylvania as a code blue state.[23] As an aside, even today Philadelphia has the reputation as the number one judicial hellhole.[24]

That is why PAPA was so adamant about advocating for meaningful tort reform. PAPA's major focus at that time was to seek legislation setting caps on non-economic damages, as there was no limit to the amount that could be awarded to a plaintiff for pain and suffering.

Placing caps on non-economic damages as had been done in California many years earlier, would limit exorbitant rewards for pain and suffering, but would not limit economic damages for medical expenses, loss of income, and so on. In its March 3, 2003 report,[25] the Office of the Assistant Secretary for Planning and Evaluation, a subdivision of the U.S. Department of Health and Human Services, cited a leading study[26] looking at the effects of our malpractice system on health-care expenditures in older patients with heart disease. The authors concluded that malpractice reforms that limit liability, such as caps on non-economic damages, could reduce health-care costs by 5–9%. At that time, the annual health-care expenditures were estimated to be $1.4 trillion annually, so a savings of 5–9% would amount to $70–126 billion per year. As noted, those annual health-care costs have since increased to $3.8 trillion per year as of 2019, which means that based on this study, tort reform, such as capping non-economic damages, could result in possible health-care cost savings of $190–342 billion per year.

PAPA lobbied and educated legislators, especially the governor, to no avail. To make a stronger statement, PAPA subsequently organized a rally to be held in Valley Forge in April 2003.[23] This was at about the time of the Iraqi invasion, and the U.S. government had developed a set of personality identification playing cards to delineate the most wanted members of the Iraqi government. The ace of spades was reserved for Saddam Hussein.[27] Along those lines, PAPA had similar cards displayed on signs at the rally, with Governor Rendell placed on the ace of spades to make a statement in their quest for tort reform. Needless to say, the comparison was not well received, but again passions were very high at the time. This was my first real taste of political activism and it made me feel part of something bigger than myself.

I began to ponder just how many other physicians were affected by malpractice lawsuits. I therefore devised a survey to get the answer for myself. At first, the survey was restricted to doctors at two hospitals where I had privileges, but with the help of PAPA, I was able to send out over 5,000 surveys to physicians across the state and received more than 1,000 responses. The survey questions were as noted in Figure 1.

The results were astonishing to me and demonstrated a much bigger problem than I had anticipated. I received 1,074 responses, of which only two were discarded for lack of clarity. Only 761 of the respondents specifically answered question 1, although all of the 1.072 physicians completed the rest of the survey, encompassing a total of 1,212 lawsuits. The results are displayed in Tables 1, 2, and 3.

1. Have you ever been sued?   Yes _____   No _____

2. Have you been sued in the last 5 years?   Yes _____   No_____

If you answered no to question 2, you are done. If yes, please continue.

3. How many times have you been sued IN THE LAST 5 YEARS?   _____

4. Of these suits (last 5 years only), how many resulted in:

                                    Case dropped   _____

                                    Case settled   _____

                                    Case lost in court   _____

                                    Case won in court   _____

                                    Case is pending   _____

5. Of the cases settled, how many were settled due to undue pressure even
    though you felt that no malpractice was committed?

Figure 1. Physician survey regarding lawsuit experiences

The data were remarkable in a number of aspects. The most important finding was that more than two-thirds of physicians reported having ever experienced a lawsuit. The data did not distinguish between physicians at the end of their careers versus physicians who were just starting out. Thus, the 70.6% of physicians who had ever been sued was probably an underestimate of the likelihood of being sued in one's career, as physicians just starting out would be

Table 1. Number of doctors experiencing lawsuits within last five years

Lawsuits in last 5 years	0	1	2	3	4	>4	Total
# of doctors	487	281	157	68	27	52	1072
Cases dropped		83	133	77	45	123	461
Cases settled		39	42	19	14	25	139
Cases lost in court		2	8	1	2	8	21
Cases won in court		28	26	13	7	29	103
Cases still pending		129	105	94	40	120	488
Total		281	314	204	108	305	1212
Cases settled w/o merit		34	37	15	14	22	122

Table 2. Results of 1,212 lawsuits among 1,072 doctors

			%	#
% of doctors ever sued	537	761	70.6	
Of total suits last 5 years				
% of doctors with 1 or more suits pending	340	1072	31.7	
% of doctors sued	585	1072	54.6	
# of suits/MD	1212	1072		1.1
# of suits/MD being sued	1212	585		2.1
% of suits dropped	461	1212	38.0	
% of suits settled	139	1212	11.5	
% of suits lost	21	1212	1.7	
% of suits won	103	1212	8.5	
% of suits pending	488	1212	40.3	

Table 3. Results of 724 lawsuits that reached conclusion

Of non-pending suits			
% of suits dropped	461	724	63.7
% of suits settled	139	724	19.2
% of suits lost	21	724	2.9
% of suits won	103	724	14.2

unlikely to have been sued. A number of physicians made reference in their surveys that they had just started their careers.

A second point to note is that more than half of all physicians had been sued within the five years just prior to the survey, with almost one in three involved in at least one active lawsuit at the time of the survey. Most of the cases did not result in an award for the plaintiff, yet still a majority of physicians reported having had a recent lawsuit. This suggests a system where the awards that accrue to plaintiffs and their lawyers are enough to generate a large number of lawsuits, despite only an approximately one in five chance of winning some award.

Perhaps the most striking finding of the survey was in the responses to question 5 (noted in Table 1) where 122 of the 139 physicians who settled a lawsuit did so due to undue pressure, even though they felt that no malpractice had been committed. I was one of them.

My results have been supported by a more recent Medscape study in 2017 of over 4,000 physicians, in which 55% of them reported having been named in a lawsuit.[28] Eighty-nine percent of these physicians felt that the suit was unwarranted. Thirty-two percent of cases were settled, but this study did not specifically address any correlation between the feeling that the case lacked merit, and willingness to settle as my survey did. Thirty-eight percent of physicians reported that the ultimate outcome was unfair, even though only 2% of cases resulted in a jury verdict for the plaintiff.

The conclusion to be reached was that the potential for a jackpot verdict outweighed the merit of a case, such that plaintiffs and their attorneys could afford to lose approximately four out of five cases and still do well, with the awards more than enough to compensate for the expenditures in non-meritorious cases. This, in conjunction with physicians' willingness to settle a non-meritorious case, meant that almost any lawsuit had the potential to be a winner regardless of whether there was any wrongdoing on the physician's part. As I mentioned earlier, lawyers have argued that they do not file frivolous lawsuits. The evidence indicates otherwise.

A study in the *New England Journal of Medicine* looked at 1,452 closed malpractice claims.[29] In 37 of these cases (3%), the patient did not even sustain a verifiable medical injury, yet six of these patients (16%) actually received a payment (Figure 2). In 515 of the patients (37%), no medical error was identified, but 145 of them (28%) received payment. That means that in a group of 552 plaintiffs who had either no injury or no medical error, more than 25% of them received compensation. Patients who have been legitimately injured due to malpractice should receive fair compensation, but this is incomprehensible.

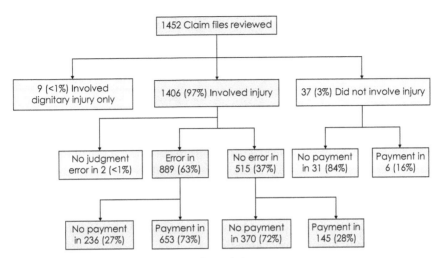

Figure 2. Results of 1452 malpractice claims

Note: Copyright Massachusetts Medical Society/Reprinted with permission

The flip side is that there are also patients who have been legitimately injured but are not appropriately compensated. According to a study by an attorney in the *New England Journal of Medicine,* only 17% of patients injured by malpractice received compensation.[30] He argued that physicians do not necessarily get sued even when there is good reason to do so and described that negligent injuries are 7.6 times more common than actual claims. It is understandable that there will be inherent bias in these studies, depending on whether one is a physician or a plaintiff's attorney, but the bottom line is that we are not getting it right often enough. Patients who sue and receive compensation are not necessarily victims of negligence, and patients who are victims of negligence do not necessarily sue. All of this speaks to a badly broken system that was not achieving its goals and needed to be overhauled. This explains why physicians in the early 2000s were so disenchanted with the system in place. It accounts for the high degree of agitation among physicians, such that PAPA could take the incredible action of putting Governor Rendell on the ace of spades, analogous to Saddam Hussein, at their rally. On a personal level, I experienced a tremendous sense of relief to learn that I was not alone, and that being sued did not make me a bad doctor or a bad person. It was simply part of the price you paid for being a doctor. Nothing personal, strictly business. It also motivated me to advocate for tort reform, which was the number one medical issue in the early 2000s.

While caps on non-economic damages never became a reality in Pennsylvania, there were some changes made in 2002–2003 that did improve the malpractice environment. Act 13, the MCARE act, was passed in 2002[31] and addressed the three critical areas of patient safety, legal reform, and insurance reform.[32] Most importantly, it specified requirements for expert witness testimony, with the goal of limiting lawsuits without merit. Act 13 established that experts who would testify to wrongdoing must possess an unrestricted license to practice medicine, must be engaged in or retired from active clinical practice or teaching within the last five years, and must practice and be board certified in the same subspecialty as the defendant. This was to become important to me a few years later when the State Board of Medicine ignored these requirements in their use of an "expert" witness against me.

A similar critical change was the Supreme Court of Pennsylvania mandate for a certificate of merit prior to a lawsuit being filed.[33] This ruling decreed that an attorney must file documentation that:

> an appropriate licensed professional has supplied a written statement that there exists a reasonable probability that the care, skill or knowledge exercised or exhibited in the treatment, practice or work that is the subject of the complaint, fell outside acceptable professional standards and that such conduct was a cause in bringing about the harm.

In other words, plaintiffs' attorneys were now required to provide documentation, *before* they filed a lawsuit, that a physician had reviewed the case and felt that the care provided was unacceptable. Had this ruling existed at the time of my first lawsuit, filed by CK, the case would never have been filed, as the plaintiff's attorney was never able to provide such documentation. I would have been spared two and a half years of anxiety. Unfortunately, the certificate of merit is not subject to scrutiny, so some physicians will act as hired guns in this regard, willing to say anything for a price, without any fear of repercussion. I personally experienced this a few years later.

The MCARE act also mandated changes in joint and several liability.[34] In 2002, the rule was that a defendant was 100% responsible for the judgment, even if they had played a minimal role in causing damages. The MCARE act eliminated that, such that now a defendant was only responsible for paying their "fair share" of the damages. This has gone back and forth over the years, but on June 28, 2011, Pennsylvania Governor Tom Corbett signed into law Senate Bill 1131, better known as the "Fair Share Act."[35] Once again, if this rule had been in place at the time of my second lawsuit, it likely would have influenced my decision to settle. It should be noted that even today, this ruling remains controversial, as a recent decision suggests that the Fair Share Act can be bypassed.[36]

Finally, the legislature also updated rules regarding venue for medical liability cases in 2003. Act 27–2002 added a provision to the Judicial Code dictating that medical professional liability cases could only be filed in the county where the alleged malpractice action had taken place.[37] One of the key reasons I settled my second lawsuit was because of venue, so venue reform was a major accomplishment. Again, had this been in place at the time of my lawsuit, I may not have been willing to settle. The venue issue was to rear its head again in 2020 and remains an ongoing point of contention. In 2018, the Civil Procedural Rules Committee of the Supreme Court of Pennsylvania published a proposed rule change to the existing venue rule. This has been hotly debated with physicians strongly protesting this idea. If the Supreme Court reverts back to its pre-2003 decision, we may be headed for another malpractice crisis in Pennsylvania.

Indeed the malpractice landscape has improved with these changes. Table 4 below demonstrates the number of lawsuits filed in Montgomery County, a suburb of Philadelphia, and in Philadelphia itself from 2000 to 2018.[38]

The changes from the 2000–2003 period to the 2004–2007 period are especially noteworthy considering that the legislative and judicial changes were enacted in 2002 and 2003. There has been a significant decrease in the number of lawsuits filed in Philadelphia over an approximately 15-year period. This is vital because the percentage of verdicts in favor of the plaintiff from 2014 to 2018 was 12.5% for Montgomery County and 34.4% for Philadelphia.[38] As a result, defendants are more likely to settle a lawsuit in Philadelphia and more reluctant to settle a lawsuit in Montgomery County. This is why venue is such an important issue and why the trial bar supports venue shopping.

Table 4. Incidence of lawsuits in Montgomery and Philadelphia Counties

Years	Montgomery	Philadelphia
2000–2003	20	1047
2004–2007	101	564
2008–2011	87	461
2012–2014	93	384
2015–2018	107	395

Nonetheless, despite the ongoing venue issue, the malpractice climate has cooled off considerably. We are not hearing about a malpractice crisis in Pennsylvania now as we were 20 years ago. The need for tort reform remains an ongoing issue, but other health-care issues have surpassed it in importance in the ensuing years and it has fallen out of the spotlight.

Chapter 4

Politics

There were multiple other things occurring simultaneously in the years after my lawsuits besides my newfound willingness to put my thoughts on paper. Despite the legislative changes, there was still incredible animosity between the legal and medical professions, with each side blaming the other for the problems that existed. I must confess that I personally did not feel too kindly toward plaintiffs' attorneys.

Through PAPA, I had the opportunity to meet legislators for the first time. At that time, the need for tort reform was supported primarily by Republicans and I gravitated to that side of the aisle on that basis. That was the only issue that really mattered to me and I was attracted to candidates who understood the need for reform.

The most notable candidate was Ellen Bard, who was running for Congress in 2004. She was a strong advocate for the need to address the malpractice crisis. I had become rather outspoken, and I was quite passionate when I was afforded the opportunity to speak at political rallies on Ellen's behalf (See Figure 3). I also wore my heart on my sleeve when I wrote op-eds in support of Ellen, such as the following in November 2003:

IT IS TIME

Two years ago, I couldn't tell you the difference between a Democrat and a Republican, a conservative and a liberal. So why am I now writing to request that you donate money to a political candidate? The answer lies in my experience and in the experience of the **70%** (yes 70%) of Pennsylvania physicians OF ALL SPECIALTIES who have been sued at least once in their careers. (It's not just the surgeons and OB/GYNs.)

I have been victimized twice by frivolous lawsuits, and I speak from the heart when I say that these have been devastating to my psyche. I could not fight back at the time, but now I am fighting back in the only way I can, by becoming political. This means learning about the issue in depth, learning which candidates favor tort reform, and supporting (i.e., donating money to and publicizing) them.

Ellen Bard has been an advocate for physicians for years. She has been staunch in proposing tort reform measures and standing up to the trial attorneys' lobby. She has supported us and our response back has been, to put it simply, inadequate. The trial attorneys know that donations to political candidates will maintain their position of strength. They out donate us by a **WIDE** margin.

It is time to turn the tables! It is time to stand up to the bullies! It is time to take back our profession! It is time to protect our patients' right to be able to access health care! If we can't or won't stand up for our patients, who will? Will a donation to Ellen guarantee a change in the status quo? Unfortunately, no. I can assure you however that a failure to fight back ensures that physicians, and therefore our patients, will lose!

This is why I am urging you to make a donation to Ellen in the amount of $500, $1,000, or whatever you can afford. If you have never donated before, now would be a good time to start. If you think this is expensive, you are correct, but as physicians, we can't afford to lose this battle. We can't afford not to give.

IT IS TIME!

Your help is greatly appreciated.

Mark Lopatin, MD.

Ellen lost the primary to ophthalmologist Melissa Brown and I was upset, but not for very long. After the primary, Melissa called me to ask for my support in her race against the incumbent Democrat, Allyson Schwartz. I was shocked to learn that I was being heard and that my voice mattered to a candidate. I discussed the importance of tort reform with Melissa and I agreed to support her thereafter. I campaigned for Melissa against Allyson, but alas, Allyson won that election. I would confront Allyson two years later on her positions and her behavior.

On another front, I was also helping to organize "Time Outs" at Abington Hospital. These consisted of time set aside every Tuesday where as many physicians as possible would leave their practice at noon for half an hour to march in front of the hospital, carrying signs protesting the malpractice crisis. My sign said, "Sick? Call a Lawyer," with the implication that lawyers were controlling health care. A protest by physicians was quite striking (no pun intended) at the time. Imagine a large group of doctors actually picketing outside a hospital. The story made national news, and an AP photographer took a picture of the protests, which was featured in *Time* and in *USA Today* with my sign front and center (See Figure 4).

Figure 3. Speaking at a rally for Ellen Bard

Note: Copyright MediaNews Group/Reprinted with permission

Figure 4. Protesting for tort reform outside of Abington hospital
Note: AP photo/Jacqueline Larma/Reprinted with permission

In the interim, my voice was being heard in other arenas. The field representative for the Montgomery County Medical Society (MCMS) approached me with regard to coming to a board of trustees meeting. I knew nothing of organized medicine at the time, but I must admit I was flattered. I attended several meetings and shortly thereafter, I was offered a position on the board, which I accepted. I also joined the Pennsylvania Medical Society (PAMED).

While I was campaigning for Ellen, I also became involved in the 2004 race for Pennsylvania state representative in the 153rd district, with Josh Shapiro running against Jon Fox. I was asked to support Jon with the idea that he was physician-friendly. Josh was a relative unknown at the time. His father, Steve, was a pediatrician on staff at Abington Hospital where I was also on staff, but I did not know him. The major deciding factor for me in this election was that the trial bar had donated money to Josh, which immediately turned me against him. If the trial bar wanted him, then I didn't. Josh asserted that he would support physicians, but I had doubts as to whether a freshman legislator would be able to stand up to his party. I had no reason to believe that he could. I was later proven very wrong.

In October of 2004, I was scheduled to travel to Hershey for the annual meeting of the Pennsylvania Medical Society House of Delegates, which was starting the next day. Before I left, I had plans to attend the Abington Hospital talent show where my wife Suzan was performing. As I approached the door to enter the event, Steve accosted me, asking me how I could possibly support Jon instead of his son. I did not know Steve at all and was taken aback that he even knew who I was. Once again, the lesson I learned was that when you speak, people do pay attention. I was somewhat tongue-tied when he approached me, as I was never one to do well with confrontation. Nonetheless, I promised Steve that if Josh won, I would do everything in my power to work with him. When Josh eventually won the election, I kept my word and sent him a congratulatory email.

A few years later, a critical vote was taking place on the issue of joint and several liability. Josh's vote was not supposed to matter, but as it turned out, the vote was very close. The Democrats exerted tremendous pressure, but Josh held his ground and supported physicians. His decision was not popular within his own party, and he later told me that he ate dinner alone that night. His courage and integrity earned my respect and I have been an ardent supporter since then.

The other irony is that since that night, I have gotten to know Steve much better as we have served together on both the county and state medical society boards of trustees. He has demonstrated himself to be someone who acts with principles and passion, and he has become a friend. Our initial adversarial encounter has become nothing more than a footnote to our shared political advocacy.

I was not shy about speaking my mind regarding the need for tort reform. Shortly after I had agreed to serve on the board of trustees of the county medical society, the chairman asked me if I would chair the Montgomery County Medical Legal Committee. This position offered me the opportunity to interact with lawyers directly. I had the chance to hear opposing viewpoints, some of which made sense, and some of which were absurd, such as the idea that frivolous lawsuits do not occur, or that the costs of malpractice are not that high. Mostly, however, I was forced to see lawyers as individual people rather than as a generic group, which was another valuable lesson for me. Generalizations based on race or religion are generally accepted as abhorrent, but I had thought nothing of generalizations based on someone's profession, especially if that profession was law. I was wrong. Just as in any other profession, including medicine, there are good attorneys and bad attorneys, honest ones and ones who do not care about the truth. In fact, the most reprehensible person I ever met in my career was not a lawyer, but instead a member of my own profession.

Through the medical legal committee, I worked side by side with attorneys on several projects, including a medical legal code of ethics, a guide to ethical behaviors that lawyers and physicians should engage in when interacting with each other. Given the hostile legal environment, I organized a seminar entitled "Finding Common Ground" which looked for issues that lawyers and doctors could agree upon, in the hope of bridging the gap between the two professions. This was later followed up with "Anatomy of a Lawsuit," a program which we ran several times, whose objective was to help physicians understand and cope with what happens when one gets sued. It was also designed to help lawyers realize how lawsuits affect physicians. The expression, "Nothing personal, just business" simply does not apply. Physicians take lawsuits against them very personally. Perhaps the most important issue I worked on was the investigation of mediation as an alternate means of dispute resolution for medical malpractice lawsuits. To that end, the Montgomery County Task Force on Mediation was created in 2005 under the auspices of the Supreme Court of Pennsylvania, and I was asked to lead it. The task force consisted of physicians, attorneys, and mediation experts with the goal of creating a pilot program at a local hospital, which we accomplished in 2008.

The bottom line in all of this was that I became very involved in trying to find meaningful ways for physicians and lawyers to work together. I had taken the bitter lemons from my legal experiences and tried to make lemonade out of them. This proved to be helpful in my healing process.

In the meantime, Allyson Schwartz won her election in 2004 and was running for reelection in 2006. I had the opportunity to meet her in person when she came to my synagogue for a "Meet the Candidates" session, just a few weeks before the election.

Although the changes made by the legislature in 2002 and 2003 were helpful, there still was a malpractice crisis going on and caps on non-economic damages was still a hot-button item in 2006. I posed a question to her regarding the need for tort reform and her position on caps. She responded to the audience that if caps were placed on non-economic damages, injured people would not be compensated adequately. She completely ignored the concept that these people would be compensated appropriately for their economic damages. I was appalled that she would disseminate this false information. I approached her after the program ended to discuss the issue with my then 13-year-old daughter by my side. Allyson proceeded to turn her back on me and completely ignored what I was saying. At this point, I was livid, but there was not much I could do except to write the following letter:

Dear Congresswoman Schwartz,

I am writing to thank you for appearing at the Meet the Candidates Breakfast at Temple Beth Am on Sunday, October 15. I appreciate your taking time out of your busy schedule to attend.

I am the physician who posed the question to you regarding the need for tort reform. I must say I was somewhat taken aback by your responses. It is clear to me that you wanted no part of any discussion regarding med mal reform. You stated that you support tort reform in all areas except for caps, yet nowhere on your website do you even mention the need for tort reform as an issue. You also dismissed the topic on that day. You stated to the audience that we disagree about caps, but you misinformed them with regard to caps, by stating that $250,000 is not enough to compensate someone who has been severely injured. You completely misrepresented the fact that caps would not affect economic damages such as lost wages, health costs, special equipment, etc., but would only apply to pain and suffering. Therefore, someone who was severely injured would not be limited to $250,000. You chose to ignore this fact and presented wrong information to your audience! As a politician, you have an obligation to present the facts accurately, regardless of your opinions on them. You did not do that. This does your audience as well as you a great disservice.

Contrary to what you seemed to think, it was not my intent to badmouth lawyers. Nowhere in my question did I say anything bad about trial attorneys. I did cite the hostile legal environment, but I specifically focused on the problem of defensive medicine, which you completely ignored. In fact, I am the co-chair of the Montgomery County Medical-Legal committee. One of the areas I have been focusing on is the concept of finding common ground, areas where lawyers and physicians can agree. I am also the chair of the Montgomery County Mediation Task Force. This group of physicians and lawyers work together to promote mediation as a less hostile and more effective way to resolve disputes. In other words, I don't routinely bash lawyers. You misjudged me.

You also asserted that we should target the malpractice insurance companies. I specifically stated in my question that my focus was not on malpractice premiums, but rather on the effect of defensive medicine, which results in higher health insurance costs to patients, delayed access to care, unnecessary testing, etc. You completely missed this point.

For some physicians, it may indeed be about the cost of insurance premiums. For me, that is not and never has been the issue. It has always been about what is fair. How do we appropriately compensate those who have been victims of true negligence, without attacking a doctor who has done things right even if the outcome is less than desired? Maloccurrence does not equal malpractice. Our current system just does not do a good job of making this distinction for a variety of reasons.

Your seeming dismissal of the overall situation as a minor problem, not worthy of discussion, is incomprehensible to me. I feel that I touched a nerve, judging by your obvious annoyance with my question and subsequent discussion on that day. I raised a legitimate issue and frankly, I felt you were rude to me. There is always room for polite disagreement, but please don't dismiss the issue. This problem affects every one of your constituents, in terms of the health care they receive, and the health-care dollars they expend. Your clear unwillingness to hear me that day was disappointing. I expected more from you.

Finally, let me thank you for taking the time to read this. I do hope you will consider what I have written and give more thought to the situation. Only if we work together with honest and open discussion working toward a mutual goal with consideration for others' views can we hope to resolve these problems.

Respectfully,
Mark Lopatin, MD.

I never received a response!

Chapter 5

Private Practice

Separate from political advocacy and my legal woes, there were other incidents over the years that helped to shape me as an advocate, and more importantly, as a person. Taking care of patients in and of itself has been an education.

"PM" was a patient whom I treated for lupus while I was at MCP. In my last year there, she became quite ill on Christmas Eve. It was one of the few times in my career that I was asked to go into the hospital late at night. PM was having a lupus flare that was attacking her central nervous system. This is one of the most dangerous manifestations of the disease. It was necessary to treat her with high doses of steroids and a medicine, Cytoxan, which is a form of chemotherapy. Cytoxan is well known as a medication with significant risk of side effects. Fortunately, she managed to survive after a long and stormy course, albeit with a number of complications.

One of those complications was peritonitis, an inflammation of the lining of the abdominal organs that can be seen in lupus. I remember getting into a heated debate with the infectious disease attending physician regarding the case. He was one of my professors from medical school and residency, and I was a new attending there, so I was at a bit of a disadvantage. He insisted that we stick a needle into the abdomen to extract fluid for analysis. The likelihood of infection was low, and she was already on appropriate antibiotics, so performing the procedure was not likely to provide useful information and had potential risks. When I asked him why we should do this, he said it was important to absolutely exclude an infection. The inflammation was most likely related to her lupus, although there was no way to prove it. I felt it was entirely inappropriate to expose the patient to additional risk to get information that was unlikely to change her management.

As difficult as it was for me to confront him on this issue, I persisted. Being able to stand up to an authority figure to benefit a patient stuck (again, no pun intended) with me. It was a lesson in assertiveness that would help me in later battles when the emphasis on putting the patient first was lost.

After she recovered, PM credited me with saving her life, and decided to continue under my care, even after I left MCP in 1992. Almost a year later, her lupus flared again and she was admitted to the ICU at Abington Hospital. From her standpoint, I had recently navigated her through a life-threatening flare, and she was prepared to follow all of my recommendations to the letter. While she was hospitalized, I was also consulted on the patient in the next room in the ICU. This patient also had lupus and her case was very similar to PM's. This patient, however, was not so amenable to my recommendations. I could not convince her to take the high doses of steroids she needed to fight the disease. Her philosophy was that God would save her. Usually when a patient makes this argument, I point out that perhaps the treatment I am recommending is the mechanism by which God would save them. That did not work here. Both patients continued to be quite ill. Despite following all of my recommendations, PM ultimately died. The other patient, who had refused to follow my advice, recovered and left the hospital.

These outcomes taught me another lesson in humility. I learned not to take so much credit when a patient does well, and not to beat myself up so much when they don't. I could provide the same advice in two similar cases with completely different outcomes as had occurred here. I realized that although a patient's clinical course does depend on what I do, it also depends on many variables well beyond my individual expertise.

In rheumatology, we rarely cure patients, although we can decrease pain and the risk of joint damage. Sometimes, there is not a lot a physician can do to ease a patient's suffering. Over the years, I have learned that even if I cannot always resolve a patient's problem, I can always acknowledge their suffering. Validation is extremely beneficial to patients. This is especially true in patients with fibromyalgia, the condition that both patients who sued me were diagnosed with.

Fibromyalgia is a poorly understood pain dysfunction syndrome characterized by pain out of proportion to structural damage of the tissues. Under normal circumstances, the level of pain corresponds to the level of tissue damage. If you drop a golf ball on your toe, the pain is not as great as if you dropped a bowling ball or a cinder block on your toe. Researchers believe that in patients with fibromyalgia, the brain amplifies pain perception, which is why sufferers may have terrible pain, even though they "look fine." Patients also classically have tenderness in specific pressure points and fatigue in the absence of any objective findings in labs or imaging studies. Sleep does not refresh them and they typically wake in the morning feeling like they never slept. Patients often report feeling flu-like or as if their body is one giant bruise. Oftentimes, these patients are dismissed with the idea that, "it's all in your head." Many of these patients have underlying depression or anxiety and an inordinate number have a history of sexual abuse at a young age.

I typically explain to these patients that pain is an alarm system and serves a protective role, similar to a fire alarm. The sound of a fire alarm is very loud and quite unpleasant, but it warns people to leave the building. Likewise, the pain of a broken ankle is unpleasant, but it warns patients not to bear weight on the ankle in order to prevent further damage. In fibromyalgia, the pain system sustains a short circuit such that the alarm goes off even if no fire is present. The patient experiences pain, even in the absence of underlying structural damage. Imagine calling the fire company when the fire alarm goes off and having them tell you that since they did not find a fire, the alarm did not ring. You must have imagined it! They have totally dismissed you by failing to consider that maybe the electrical wiring is the problem, and that the alarm rang for the wrong reason. Patients with fibromyalgia are often told that their pain is not real. To me, it is the height of arrogance when a physician concludes that a patient's symptom does not exist unless they can find an etiology for it. I had one young patient with fibromyalgia tell me that another physician once patted her on her head and told her, "There, there, dear. There is nothing really wrong with you. You just need to get pregnant"!

Many physicians assume that fibromyalgia is simply anxiety or depression and dismiss the symptoms on that basis. The symptoms may in fact be related to underlying emotional issues. That does not make them any less important. There are numerous examples in medicine of an emotional stressor producing physical discomfort. Some even have names such as "stress ulcer" or "tension headache." The example I always use is blushing where an emotional stimulus such as telling someone that their fly is open produces the objective physical response of reddening of the face.

With this in mind, I strive to make it a point to listen to my patients with fibromyalgia and to acknowledge them, even when I cannot identify or ease their pain. Taking patients seriously and validating their complaints is a critical aspect of patient care. One patient in particular comes to mind in this regard.

"JK" was a 50-year-old woman who came to me after suffering from widespread pain for many years. Despite seeing numerous doctors, she had never received a medical diagnosis that could explain her misery, or effective treatment to address it. She told me she was certain she had rheumatoid arthritis. She described terrible stiffness every morning, but her joints were not swollen. Actually, she said, her pain didn't involve just her joints. Every muscle in her body hurt. She described constant exhaustion but was unable to sleep at night. She also suffered from depression. When I examined her, I noted that her muscles were quite tender in a characteristic distribution and her joints were not swollen. I diagnosed her with fibromyalgia.

Because sexual abuse is so common in patients with fibromyalgia, I routinely ask patients in whom I suspect fibromyalgia if they have ever been molested, assaulted, or raped. When I asked JK this question, she immediately averted her eyes and softly said yes. She proceeded to tell me that she had been molested as a child.

I asked if she had ever received counseling for this and she said no. I then asked her what her primary care physician had said about this. She informed me that she had never notified him of this. I asked her if her husband knew about it. She said no.

"So the only people who know about this are you and me?" I asked.

"Yes," she answered, as she continued to avoid my eyes.

I asked permission to inform her primary care physician of this history as I felt it was critical to her care. Her response was startling! Still staring at the floor, JK nodded and said quietly, "Yes, you can tell him. I don't think he will tell anyone."

In that instant, I realized how much shame she had been carrying around for 40 years for something that was not her fault. Her main concern all those years was making sure that no one would find out about what had happened. There was no doubt in my mind that her widespread pain, thought by her to be due to a form of arthritis, was in fact related to this emotional trauma so many years earlier. I have theorized that emotional or sexual trauma, which is too painful to deal with emotionally, may well manifest as physical pain, which in many cases is easier for the patient to deal with. That did not make JK's pain any less real or any less important.

This case was an example where listening to the whole patient rather than just treating the symptom was important. Treating her with a painkiller or arthritic medication would not have solved her problems. She was not in need of rheumatologic care to treat her physical pain. She needed to see a therapist to address the root of her pain. The problem is that too often when you advise a patient that they might benefit from counseling, it comes across as a dismissal of their symptoms. I did my best to reassure her that I knew that her pain was real, as I gently recommended counseling. Unfortunately, she never returned to my office and I do not know if she followed my recommendation. Nonetheless, the case emphasizes the importance of treating the whole patient, not just the symptoms.

This was also made clear to me when I treated another patient, "DM." I had heard of dissociative identity disorder before, but I had never seen an actual case until I met DM. There was no question that she truly had this disorder. She initially presented to me with chronic widespread pain. She also had a history of having been molested at a young age. Her pain was not arthritic in nature. I tried everything I could to address her pain, but to no avail. She was already in counseling, and there was nothing I could do to help her except to listen and validate her. I was not smart enough to realize that just by listening to her and validating her, I was providing a therapeutic benefit. She insisted on seeing me every three months, even after I had told her I could not help her.

As I got to know her better, she began to let me see one or more of the other personalities. It was fascinating in that these were completely different entities with different voices, different affects, and even different physical exams. At one of her visits, she presented with wrist pain. She had significant local tenderness on exam, and I planned to inject her wrist with cortisone. While I was preparing the syringe, one of the other personalities came out, who was not having wrist pain. The same wrist was considerably less tender on the physical exam of this second personality. Finally, a third personality came out, and this time, the wrist was not tender at all. The same person had three different physical exams. The question now became whether or not to inject the wrist, given the variable exams. Ultimately, I opted not to, but the important aspect was to recognize the totality of my patient and all of her multiple personalities.

I have emphasized the importance of the patient-physician relationship. That was never more obvious to me than when I treated "AS." AS was diagnosed with rheumatoid arthritis in September of 2003. She also had a significant problem with anxiety, for which she was receiving long-standing medication. She was well aware of her anxious tendencies and of her propensity to overreact. I adjusted her arthritis medications over the years and she did quite well. Despite that, she insisted on visits every three months for reassurance. Although her arthritis was well controlled, her anxiety would wax and wane. She was self-deprecating about her anxiety and we were able to joke about it together. We established a very good rapport and I looked forward to her visits.

In March of 2013, she called me complaining of problems with balance, dizziness, and falling. She was concerned that this might be a side effect of one of her arthritis medications. She was under significant stress as her mother was ill in another state and she was traveling back and forth frequently. She reported to me that her anxiety level was quite high.

In view of the new symptoms, I scheduled her for an appointment the next day. She appeared very anxious, which was not unusual. Her examination was normal for her, except for mild but definite weakness of the left hamstring.

She was a runner so this may well have been a running injury. It was conceivable that her complaints of dizziness and falling were simply a manifestation of her anxiety and stress. As noted, it also may have been a side effect of one of the medications being used to treat her arthritis. It would have been very easy to dismiss her symptoms as being due to anxiety. After all, the weakness on exam was subtle. However, because I had followed her for so many years, I knew there was something else going on other than just her anxiety. She did not pass the "look test,"—that gut feeling that so often is helpful in determining how to proceed. Given her description of balance problems and dizziness, along with isolated weakness, I ordered an MRI of her head.

The MRI revealed a large, potentially life-threatening subdural bleed. She had emergency surgery that night to evacuate the bleed. Seven years later, she is doing well with her arthritis well controlled and no neurologic deficits.

Continuity of care basically saved her life. It is an example of why I preach so passionately about the importance of the patient-physician relationship. This concept is being dismissed more and more while the idea that physicians are interchangeable with those who have less training has proliferated. People seek convenience in their medical care. Minute clinics at the local pharmacy with nurse practitioners as the primary providers, or doc-in-a-box facilities have sprouted up across the country. However these arrangements cannot replicate the value of a long-standing relationship between a patient and a physician who knows them well. My patient would certainly attest to that.

Then there was my Nazi patient, who also forced me to learn more about myself. It was the eve of Yom Kippur. I wanted to get home to my family in time for the holiday. At 2:30 in the afternoon, my receptionist informed me of a consult in the hospital. I would have to finish my office hours and then head over to the hospital to see the patient. A consult typically adds an hour to my day, so right off the bat, I was not looking forward to seeing this patient.

I finished office hours at about 5:00 p.m. and headed to the hospital. I reviewed the chart and found nothing particularly striking. Then I entered the room and was stunned by what I saw. The man was covered with tattoos of swastikas! On the eve of Yom Kippur, no less! A million thoughts immediately flooded my brain: My responsibility is to care for him to the best of my ability, but being Jewish, how do I block out the hatred toward me that is conveyed all over his body? Do I really have to try to help him as my Hippocratic Oath demands? What if this hatred is expressed during my time evaluating him? Should I say something? Should I simply leave? What if he needs follow up in the office? Can I really take him on as a patient or is that too great a conflict for me? My professionalism and my personal priorities were at odds with each other.

Yom Kippur teaches us to be forgiving toward others, so it was quite ironic that of all the days of the year, this was the day that I was asked to see this man. I was able to take my personal hat off and put my physician hat on. That is what a professional does, but admittedly, it was not easy. I asked him questions about his illness and examined him. Fortunately, his issue was "one and done." I was able to address the issue on that one visit. He would not need follow up in the office, and I would not be faced with the dilemma of what to do in that scenario. I remember thinking that there was no way I would be able to take this man on as a patient after discharge. I am a doctor, but I am still human and the conflict would have been too great. Nonetheless, I did what my profession requires, and I went home for Yom Kippur dinner knowing that I had done the right thing. That day emphasized my own emotions and the importance of maintaining my professionalism even under adverse circumstances.

Humanity in medicine does not just apply to how physicians see patients. Physicians must recognize that we are human too, and that our imperfections can affect the care we provide. We have our own emotions and personal stressors that we deal with. At times, it can be very difficult to block them out when one is seeing patients. Shortly after I settled my lawsuit, I saw a new patient who was referred to me for advice regarding the possible use of immunosuppressive drugs to treat her autoimmune sensorineural hearing loss. This was the same diagnosis that the patient who sued me had been given. The wound from that lawsuit was still too fresh for me, and I was simply unable to see this patient solely on the basis of her diagnosis. My professionalism was not able to overcome my own emotions in this particular case. Fortunately, I recognized my limitation, explained the situation to the patient and referred her to one of my partners. She was not happy after having waited so long to see me, but as I said, physicians are not perfect. I certainly am not.

Another situation where my emotions interfered with my ability to properly care for a patient occurred in 2020. I wrote about my experience in an article entitled "Are Physicians Allowed To Be Human?"[39]

> I knew Friday was not going to be a good day.
>
> A leak in the ceiling of my family room. A pet who would need surgery. I was already stressed well before Friday.
>
> But at work, the issues started on Thursday with an osteoporotic patient for whom I had recommended Forteo six weeks earlier. It was denied by her insurer who wanted Tymlos instead. No big deal. We simply precertified Tymlos, but this was also denied. Why? Because she had not received other treatment. They must have missed the part where the patient had taken Fosamax and not tolerated it. Now, in order to get her medication approved, I would have to do a peer to peer sometime on Friday morning, based on *the insurer's* schedule. Needless to say, I was angry that I had to jump through their hoops to make sure my patient got the care she needed.
>
> Then came the phone call Thursday afternoon. A patient of my partner, who was on vacation at the time, was being discharged from a hospital where we no longer make rounds. The hospitalist and the patient's family were not happy that we could not see her in the hospital and wanted her seen on Friday. She had been admitted with an acute inflammatory arthritis and was started on high-dose steroids. She was scheduled on Friday morning with one of our nurse practitioners. This would require supervision which would add at least 15–30 minutes to my already packed schedule.
>
> I started patient hours at 7:00 a.m. and was already 30 minutes behind when I started to see my 9:30 patient. She was a long-standing RA patient with significant joint damage of her right elbow, left wrist, and both knees. She had previously been on Remicade many years earlier, but did not tolerate it, and over the years was repeatedly unwilling to try another biologic. I was left to manage her with methotrexate alone. She did not want steroids. She did not want surgery. She did not want a biologic. We talked about injections, but she was not

really interested. Understandably, she was quite frustrated by the limited options. As I concluded the 25 minute visit, (I was now 40 minutes behind with my partner's patient and the peer to peer still looming) she then decided that she wanted her elbow injected.

My knee jerk response was, "I wish you had told me that 25 minutes ago."

Now let me state that I was wrong to say this. Note that I did not refuse to do the injection. In fact, as soon as I said this, I realized my mistake and offered to do the injection. She angrily declined and stormed out of the exam room vowing to never see me again. I gave her some time to cool off and called her two hours later to apologize. I told her that I had been stressed for time, but that that did not justify my comment. She declined my apology and stated that I was more interested in getting to my next patient. There was nothing more I could do, but I have been beating myself up since then for having said this.

Fast forward to a week later. Again it is a bad day in terms of time with a full schedule and many complicated patients who require extra time that I provide. I am quickly an hour behind. Remembering the events of a week earlier, the thought that runs through my mind is to stay calm. I remind myself that I am not supposed to be bothered when a patient cannot give me a history that makes sense, gives me conflicting information, or goes off on a tangent, all of which will make other patients wait longer. I am supposed to take in stride the time I waste clicking boxes that have no meaning. It should not matter that I have to ask multiple questions just to determine what number from 0–10 best defines their pain. Meanwhile, two other patients are waiting for me, then three, then four. After more than six straight hours of seeing patients, I realize that my bladder will soon explode and that I need to get some food into me. My morning finally ends five minutes before my first afternoon patient is scheduled, however I need some "down time" (i.e., checking labs, reviewing messages, etc.) in order to recharge my battery before starting the afternoon. I am exhausted.

So I pose the question, are physicians human? Is it acceptable for us to feel emotions? Is it OK for us to be upset when at the end of the visit, a patient brings up a new problem that will set us back an additional ten minutes? Are we justified in feeling irritated when a patient shows up late, disrupting our schedule? Are we allowed to be annoyed when we must ask permission from insurers to treat our patients?

There is an unspoken assumption that physicians should be immune to these kinds of feelings. There are tremendous expectations placed upon me by patients, insurers, pharmacies, etc. However most of the pressure comes from me as I try to be everything to everybody all of the time, even though that is not possible. I am kidding myself if I think that I can resolve every problem that is presented to me each day. All I can do is the best that I can. I must recognize that this will not always satisfy others, but it is all I can do. I must give myself permission to not be perfect. I am going to make mistakes despite my best efforts. I must realize I am allowed to have emotions such as anger or sadness. I am not an automaton. I need bathroom breaks and food. I need down time. I am human.

And sometimes I am going to say the wrong thing. I must learn to forgive myself when I do. Should I have made that statement to that patient? Absolutely not. I am a physician.

But I am also human. Now all I have to do is convince myself of that.

All of these examples emphasize the human component that is the crux of medical care, both on the patient and physician side. The patient-physician relationship is sacred and the emotion on both sides is part of that relationship and must be recognized. Balance is important, however. Physician actions based on too much emotion can be problematic as noted in the examples above. On the flip side, physicians cannot be robots, even though third parties may want us to be. Blindly following predetermined cookbook strategies is not conducive to good patient care. Every diagnosis, every treatment, and every discussion must be custom made for that individual patient, as each patient has their own specific needs. It is imperative that physicians see and understand patients as individual people, with their own desires, fears, and passions. What is right for one patient may not be right for the next. There must be guidelines, but they cannot be uniformly applied to every patient without any thought. Guidelines have become mandates in too many cases. Physicians are often forced to administer what they perceive to be less-than-optimal care due to insurance constraints. Physician loss of autonomy in caring for patients has become a major problem.

This is seen at multiple levels as middlemen infiltrate health care and dictate how care must be provided. This can range from insurers dictating choice of medications to hospital administrators who dictate how physicians see patients or even the time allotted for each patient. The graph in Figure 5 demonstrates the growth of administrators and physicians over an almost 40-year period. The number of physicians doubled while the number of administrators increased thirtyfold in the same time period. Follow up data from 2009–2020 reveals that the trend has continued along the same trajectory.[40] In the meantime, the costs of health care have skyrocketed. As noted by economist Thomas Sowell, "It is amazing that people who think we cannot afford to pay for doctors, hospitals, and medication, somehow think we can afford to pay for doctors, hospitals, medication, and a government bureaucracy to administer it."[41]

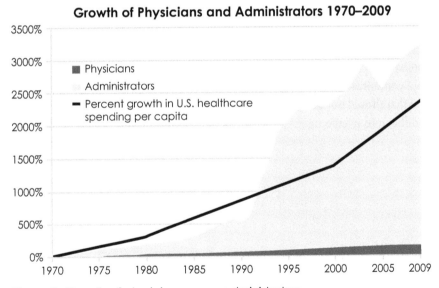

Figure 5. Growth of physicians versus administrators

Sources: Bureau of Labor Statistics; NCHS; and Himmelstein/Woolhandler analysis of CPS. Health care costs: A primer, The Henry J. Kaiser family foundation

The end result of this is a system where assembly line medicine is promoted, and physician autonomy is sacrificed. Physician burnout is rampant, with 42% of physicians describing themselves as burnt out, according to a 2020 survey.[42] Contributing factors to this epidemic include too many bureaucratic tasks and too many hours worked, along with lack of respect, control, and autonomy.[43]

Physician suicide rates are more than twice the rate of the general population[44] with approximately 300–400 physician suicides every year.[45] According to Pamela Wible, MD, one of the nation's foremost authorities on physician suicide, one million Americans lose their doctors to suicide each year.[46]

The human aspect is being sucked out of health care by corporate entities seeking to control the health-care dollar. This is not an accident. As noted by Richard Gunderman, MD, hospital executives seek to decrease physician autonomy and diminish the importance of the patient-physician relationship in order to influence the bottom line.[47]

This not only affects physicians, but more importantly, it impacts the patients we care for. One study shows that depressed and burnt-out residents are 6.2 times more likely to make a medication error.[48] Another demonstrates physician burnout is independently associated with major medical errors.[49]

There is a growing movement toward changing the term "burnout" to the term "moral injury." The former implies a lack of resilience and a failing of physicians. The latter refers to what happens when corporate entities repeatedly expect clinicians to make decisions that go against their long-standing, deeply held commitment to healing.[50] That is an issue that affects patient well-being and one that should not be ignored. Unfortunately, the widespread apathy that exists is difficult to overcome.[51]

Chapter 6

The State Board of Medicine

As I was seeing patients and getting my feet wet in the political arena, there was yet another legal case evolving. I previously compared my two lawsuits to a tropical storm and a hurricane. They were nothing compared to the tsunami that threatened to engulf me in 2004 and destroy my career in the process. It is one thing to be challenged by a patient regarding a possible malpractice action. It is another to be put on trial by the Pennsylvania State Board of Medicine. The issue involved the prescribing of opioids. The state board had an underlying agenda and they were not about to let a minor detail like the truth interfere with it. The state board was looking to make a statement to those who prescribe opioids recklessly. It did not matter that my case did not conform to their mission. I was to be their sacrificial lamb. They even went so far as to use an unqualified "expert" witness who gave false testimony against me.

I first saw the patient "TA" in January, 1996. She was a 56-year-old female with multiple psychosocial issues, who presented with chronic widespread pain. She had a history of significant depression and had been a victim of physical, emotional, and sexual abuse as a child. She had seen multiple physicians without benefit. In many cases, her symptoms had been dismissed, and she was told repeatedly that nothing could be done. Her husband accompanied her to the initial visit. I later learned that there was significant marital conflict regarding finances. He did not believe that his wife was really in pain and thought that she was merely seeking attention. He felt that the pain was "all in her head" and resented the expense of seeing so many doctors.

I evaluated her for underlying arthritic causes of chronic pain, but her workup was negative. I diagnosed her with fibromyalgia based on her history of widespread chronic pain, characteristic tender points with an otherwise negative exam, and negative lab work. I recommended counseling to address the emotional aspects of her situation. She was already on Vicodin when I first met her, but this was not adequately controlling her pain.

This was well before the opioid epidemic. In fact, physicians were being criticized for not treating pain aggressively enough at the time. There was even news of a lawsuit against a physician in California because he did not provide adequate pain relief for a dying patient.[52] In 1996, The American Pain Society had declared pain to be the fifth vital sign,[53] in addition to temperature, blood pressure, heart rate, and respiratory rate. Physicians were expected to quantify and record pain levels at each visit. The teaching was that physicians needed to be more liberal in our use of painkillers to alleviate suffering. National pain organizations taught that addiction was a function of the patient rather than the drug. They further directed that opioid doses could be escalated without a ceiling because opioids do not cause end organ damage other than respiratory depression. We were instructed to use a long-acting opioid as a maintenance drug with short-acting agents for breakthrough pain.

After evaluating TA, I began to adjust her treatment regimen by titrating her pain medication up. I subsequently placed her on the long-acting opioid OxyContin and used short-acting opioids for breakthrough pain, exactly as was recommended at the time. I assessed and reassessed her reports of pain and continued to slowly titrate the doses up, while monitoring for any adverse reaction. Keeping in mind the precepts of aggressively managing her pain, with the idea of no ceiling dose, I eventually got her up to a very high dose of OxyContin. This was less than ideal, but it was controlling her pain, and she was tolerating it without difficulty. She remained on this stable dose for a period of almost four years. It was in 2001 that my world would begin to unravel, but I would not realize it until 2004 when I was actually served with the complaint. I was absolutely terrified when I read the words "The Commonwealth of Pennsylvania, Bureau of Professional and Occupational Affairs versus Mark Alan Lopatin, MD".

TA was admitted to a hospital in July of 2001 for medical problems entirely separate from her chronic pain or use of opioids. The doctors at the hospital noted the high dose of opioids and informed the patient and her husband that this was not optimal. The doctors furthermore aroused controversy regarding the legitimacy of fibromyalgia as a diagnosis. The husband, who had questioned the validity of her pain from the outset, now became convinced that fibromyalgia did not even exist and responded by reporting me to the Pennsylvania State Board of Medicine. The request for records I received in 2004 seemed innocent enough. It was not from a lawyer and despite my prior lawsuits, which by now had been resolved, it did not register on my radar. It should have.

In general, the records request should not have been a problem. My chart was well documented with what I had done and why. However, I was not aware at the time of the state board's hidden agenda. By 2004, the use of opioids was beginning to attract attention and the state board was looking to create a deterrent to their indiscriminate use. Their concerns were not applicable to this case. I had not used opioids indiscriminately, and I felt that the documentation would indicate this. It soon became apparent that they were not interested in the facts as evidenced by the so-called expert witness they called in. It was also clear that they had no concerns about how their false accusations might affect me or my future. If they were successful in making me a scapegoat, it would mean revocation of my medical license and would destroy my ability to practice medicine.

Their expert witness, "Dr. Z," was simply a hired gun willing to do their bidding for a price. He had completed only one year of a rotating internship in family practice in the 1960s. He had not done a residency and had no rheumatology training. He had not seen a patient in 14 years and made his living providing "expert testimony." Had this been an actual malpractice lawsuit, he would have been disqualified from testifying based on the Act 13 mandates in Pennsylvania that were passed in 2002. As noted in Chapter 3, this ruling decreed that any expert who testifies must have training in the same area as the defendant and must be in active practice or recently retired. Dr. Z met neither of these criteria. That did not stop the state board of medicine from using him against me.

Dr. Z's review of my chart can only be described as stunning. I had to ask my attorney multiple times if he had actually given my entire chart to Dr. Z, as it was clear that Dr. Z had not read it carefully. He made a number of baseless attacks, such as noting the absence of a history or physical in the chart, when in fact, there was a complete history and physical in the chart. His 16-page report contained at least 25 errors of fact. It is one thing to criticize me on my choice of medications or my medical judgment; it is another to criticize me for not doing something that the chart clearly demonstrates that I did. As an example, he accused me of failing to document fibromyalgia tender points in my initial exam when this was clearly documented. He based his medical "opinions" on one superficial article on fibromyalgia. I am being generous when I say that his testimony was highly questionable in terms of its accuracy and its validity. Fraudulent would be a more appropriate word. Nonetheless, his errors and the argument that he was not qualified to testify based on Act 13 mandates fell on deaf ears. The state board noted that they were not required to follow Act 13. They simply did not care, as his testimony served their underlying agenda.

The trial was approaching in the summer of 2005 and I was a nervous wreck. My skills, competence, and most importantly, my integrity, were being impugned. I was outraged at Dr. Z's written report. My entire future was at stake against an opponent who was not interested in fairness, justice, or the truth. Suzan and I arranged for child care and we traveled to Harrisburg in July for the two-day trial.

At the trial, I finally met Dr. Z in person. He extended his hand to me and without thought, I shook it by default. I immediately regretted it. That single act of civility has haunted me since then. How could I possibly have accepted the hand of someone who was intentionally trying to destroy me without regard for the truth? I sacrificed my self-respect in that instant in the name of good manners. I have not been able to come to terms with that, even after all these years. It was truly a life-changing action for me. I was already 48 years old at the time, but I learned a lot about myself and grew up quite a bit that day. Courtesy and consideration are important but should not be rendered to those who engage in unethical behavior.

The trial then commenced. The hearing examiner allowed Dr. Z's testimony, despite his lack of qualifications. During the trial, Dr. Z continued to make ridiculous assertions that demonstrated his lack of knowledge of the current practice of medicine and more specifically the practice of rheumatology. This was not surprising as he had no rheumatology training, but it was distressing nonetheless. His oral testimony continued to demonstrate that he had not read my chart thoroughly. He repeatedly drew conclusions criticizing my care, which were not substantiated by the facts of the case. He was on the witness stand for a day and a half. It was excruciating to listen to him with the thought that the hearing examiner might find his testimony credible.

My expert witness was board certified in pain management. After he refuted the nonsense spewed by Dr. Z, it was my turn to take the stand. I did so with great apprehension and was visibly shaking as I sat there. The prosecuting attorney grilled me, but I had an answer for every question she posed. My chart was well documented on every challenge that she raised. My testimony must have been very damaging to their case against me, as I was only on the stand for 20 minutes, compared to the day and a half that Dr. Z had testified.

Then it was over. I was numb. I waited nervously for a result and tried to resume normalcy.

Seven months later, in late February 2006, the hearing examiner issued a ruling that exonerated me of all counts except for the charge that the patient had had an 11-month period where she was not seen in the office, but still received prescriptions. He therefore ruled that I must take a course approved by the state board on how to prescribe opioids. Dr. Z just so happened to run such a course. Coincidence?

The ruling by the hearing examiner specifically stated that I was "subject to disciplinary action in that I failed to meet or maintain minimum standards in regard to medical reevaluations while continuing to prescribe controlled substances." The hearing examiner overlooked the documentation that I had seen this patient 35 times prior to this 11-month period, and that she had been on a stable dose of medicine at that time for almost three years. It also ignored the fact that the patient was scheduled during this period but was not seen because she did not keep three appointments. The hearing examiner also declared in his report that "the evidence is insufficient to establish that the care and treatment rendered by Respondent constitutes unprofessional conduct in the practice of medicine." The report concluded with the statement, "It is clear that Respondent had the patient's best interest in mind."

With regard to the 11-month period that TA went without being seen, the examiner wrote, "While particularly troublesome, Respondent's prescription of OxyContin during this period of time did not drop below the minimum standard of care." Despite these words *in his own report*, he ruled against me as noted.

The state board immediately reviewed the case. They ignored subsequent briefs from the Pennsylvania Medical Society on my behalf objecting to the qualifications of the "expert." The board said that they did not need his testimony anyway, yet without his testimony, there was no case at all against me. This was befuddling and infuriating, but again was consistent with their hidden agenda.

The board issued a final ruling on July 5, 2006, approximately a year after my trial, stating that they supported the hearing examiner's position that I must take a course on prescribing opioids. The board reported that the basis for action was "unprofessional conduct," even though the hearing examiner's report specifically stated that there was insufficient evidence for unprofessional conduct.

The end result of this was that I had to take an online course on prescribing opioids that did not teach me anything that I did not already know. In fact, I probably could have taught the course. I believe this was the board's way of saving face for instituting a case that had no merit and was significantly flawed.

My next step was to investigate the possibility of a countersuit against Dr. Z and the state board. I was angry at the injustice I had experienced, but there were also financial ramifications. This was not a malpractice case, so my insurer would not cover the costs. I had paid out of pocket for my defense to the tune of about $30,000 when all was said and done.

I discussed my options with an attorney. He informed me that in order to countersue, I would have to first get a favorable ruling from the State Supreme Court, as expert witnesses and the state board have immunity. That would be an expensive proposition and not likely to succeed. I had already spent quite a bit of money and was not willing to spend more when the odds were against success. I then asked about the possibility of seeking sanctions against Dr. Z's license for his fraudulent testimony, but he was already in his late 70s and had decided not to renew his license anyway. Sanctions would be irrelevant.

I felt powerless. He had already done his damage to me emotionally. I firmly believe that I have a component of PTSD related to this case, although I have not been formally diagnosed. I did require further counseling to help me cope with this. Years later, there are still times when I tremble uncontrollably when I talk or write about it. Even now as I write about this and my other legal experiences, I am tremulous.

There were other significant ramifications of my experience. As a direct result of this case, I stopped writing prescriptions for almost all opioids. I decided that I would no longer treat chronic pain patients. Instead, I routinely referred them to pain management once I had excluded an underlying rheumatologic diagnosis. I asked questions about the state board of medicine and how it works. It was only then that I learned through some political connections about the state board's preordained agenda regarding opioids. I am lucky that my chart was well documented. This enabled me to escape from a dangerous opponent with not much more than a slap on the wrist. As a result, I cannot begin to emphasize enough the importance of thorough documentation to other physicians, medical students, and others who provide health care. Physicians are forced to document so many meaningless items in a patient's chart. It is imperative that we also document the important aspects, such as what we think, what we did or didn't do, and why or why not.

I do not hesitate to share what I endured. I recognize that there is a code of silence that must be broken when one is involved in legal action. It is imperative that we speak out to patients, legislators, and other physicians against these types of injustices. The sense of isolation can be overwhelming. I do not want anyone to go through what I have gone through, questioning myself, my skills, and my self-worth. Hopefully sharing our stories will help to give other physicians added strength. I have come to firmly believe that publicity and sharing our experiences are our best tools against legal injustice.

Despite the possible PTSD, this episode made me stronger as an individual. It was a gauntlet for me and I was able to come out the other side, albeit with some residual effects. I am more determined and more motivated in my grass-roots and medical society advocacy efforts because of what I experienced. Suzan had already described me as being like a dog with a bone, even before this. This ordeal only amplified my stubbornness and tenacity. It also brought me closer to Suzan. She was an absolute rock for me to lean on throughout this trauma.

The handshake incident was a revelation for me in terms of self-awareness and understanding how I disrespected myself in that instant. I am much more likely now to call out bad behavior rather than resorting to civil pleasantries when they are not appropriate. I have become more assertive, and I am not so willing to diminish my own thoughts in favor of others. It sounds strange, but I had to consciously process the idea that what I think has just as much value as what others think.

There was one final silver lining. The state board assured me that as a result of this case, they would subsequently apply Act 13 requirements to their experts. If they had followed this rule initially, this case would have been dismissed at the outset. I draw some solace from thinking that perhaps others will not have to suffer as much because of the emotional trauma I experienced.

PART II

REVOLUTION

Chapter 7

Prior Authorization
and Third Party Payers

"SL" was a 60-year-old gentleman, referred to me in 2013 for left ankle pain. His initial physician thought he had cellulitis, an infection of the soft tissue underneath the skin. Antibiotics did not help him, however. Subsequently, another doctor thought he might have gout, a form of arthritis caused by deposits of uric acid in the joint. Gout attacks usually last several days and then go away, but SL had been having continuous pain for two months by the time he saw me. Prior X-rays were reportedly negative for fracture and a variety of treatments had failed to help him. He had no symptoms to suggest a systemic form of arthritis, such as rheumatoid arthritis. His exam revealed swelling and marked tenderness of his left ankle. After examining him, I ordered an MRI to look for structural damage, such as a torn ligament. We needed to get approval from his insurer before he could get the MRI. My staff submitted the necessary paperwork. The insurance company denied the MRI.

My staff explained to me that his insurance would not approve an MRI unless he had experienced six weeks or more of pain, along with a negative X-ray. Both of these requirements applied to my patient, so I was not sure why the MRI had been denied. They informed me that I would need to do a "peer to peer" to get approval. During a peer to peer, the treating doctor explains to his "peer," a doctor from the insurance company, why they are recommending a particular procedure or treatment. Since my patient met both criteria, I was optimistic that obtaining insurance approval through a peer to peer would not be a problem. I was wrong.

The insurance doctor, who was not a rheumatologist, informed me that SL must have physical therapy (PT) prior to getting an MRI. This made no sense to me. When I asked the insurance doctor to explain why, she told me, "Because some patients get better with PT." I was incredulous at her rationale and informed her that it was inexcusably poor medicine and actually malpractice to ask my patient to go to PT without first knowing the anatomy of the joint. Her response was a cool, "We don't think so." I asked if this was strictly a financial decision. She told me no. She said that the insurer's "guidelines" dictated that PT should come before an MRI. She was clearly following them blindly without any true understanding of the situation.

One of the most disturbing parts of all of this was the lack of transparency. A cost decision by the insurance company was couched as a medical decision, even though it was clinically incorrect. I would have accepted it more easily if I had been told from the outset that this was a decision based strictly on money, but decisions based on cost are felt to be an anathema and are never stated, even though they occur on a regular basis. Instead, I was told that PT was what was best for my patient by a non-rheumatologist who had never even seen the patient!

There was not much I could do. SL could have paid out of pocket for the MRI, but the cost was prohibitive for him. I explained the situation and advised him to go to PT for one visit to satisfy the bureaucracy. I instructed him not to bear weight or do anything that would cause pain or further damage to his ankle. He made the token visit. I then notified the insurer that SL had gone to PT and could not tolerate it. These are the games physicians are sometimes forced to play to provide proper patient care. The insurer finally approved the MRI and it was done four weeks after I had initially ordered it. The MRI revealed an oblique fibular fracture, which had not shown up on X-ray, as the source of his pain. Had he legitimately gone to PT, he may well have injured the ankle more. If that had happened, it would have been me, not the insurance company, who would have been held legally liable. As it was, there was a significant delay in his care due to the prior authorization process, compounded by the insurer's denial of the MRI. I referred SL to an orthopedist. He was placed in a cast and did well. Two months later, he was pain-free and had no further need for rheumatologic care.

We have a tremendous problem with health-care costs in this country. The government and private insurers as third party payers are therefore looking for ways to reduce the costs of health care. One of the ways they do this is through prior authorization, also known as pre-certification. Prior authorization is a process where the insurer must approve an order for a diagnostic test or treatment before the patient can receive it. If the insurer fails to approve the test or treatment, the patient must either choose to bear the total cost or forego the test or treatment. In most cases, the cost is prohibitive. Thus, a denial by the insurer usually means that the patient will not get the test or treatment that the physician has recommended. This approval process often results in a delay or even denial of necessary treatment as occurred with SL, and is determined by an insurer who has never examined or even spoken with the patient.

The prior authorization process starts with the physician's office staff submitting medical information to the patient's insurer regarding the recommended test or treatment. This typically consists of the physician progress notes, prior studies, and any previous treatments administered to the patient. If the insurer denies care, the physician must then take the time to write a "letter of medical necessity" justifying the rationale for their recommendation. I recall writing my very first letter of medical necessity before I understood the process. I had written a prescription for Enbrel for my patient, "BG," that the insurer denied, saying it was not medically necessary. I wrote, "This letter will serve to verify the medical necessity for Enbrel for my patient, BG. Obviously, I would not have written the prescription in the first place if I did not feel it was medically necessary."

It seemed so obvious to me at the time. A physician does not recommend treatment that they feel is unnecessary. Why would an insurer even question the necessity? Do they think so little of physicians as to think we would recommend unnecessary treatments? The answer is yes! As I said, I was quite naive, especially in terms of the financial ramifications for insurers. Needless to say, my letter did not sway the insurer, and my request for Enbrel was denied. Fortunately, BG was quite wealthy and was able to afford the medication herself. Most patients are unable to do so and are at the mercy of their insurer. It remains unclear to me why an insurer, who has never evaluated the patient, is qualified to decide what is or is not medically necessary.

Insurers argue that they are not saying what is or is not medically necessary; they are merely stating what they will pay for. That is simply not true. Their communications dictate otherwise and often cast doubt upon the treating physician. They do not inform the patient that the potential benefit of the test or the treatment does not justify the cost expenditure in their opinion. Instead, they notify the patient that the physician has ordered a test or treatment that is medically unnecessary or experimental. They may report that other treatments should be tried first. A patient reading this may well begin to have reservations regarding the competence of their physician, thus damaging the patient-physician relationship.

If the letter of medical necessity fails to convince the insurer as is often the case, the next step is the peer-to-peer phone call. Most of the time, as occurred with SL, the peer is not a physician in the same specialty as the treating doctor and usually has no personal knowledge of the medical issue at hand. Sometimes the peer at the insurance company is not even a physician. There have been times when I have had to get approval from a nurse or a pharmacist.

When the peer has no expertise in a particular area of medicine, they will often resort to predetermined cookie-cutter "guidelines" that may or may not even apply to the patient at hand. This again is what happened in SL's case where the peer was not a rheumatologist and had no understanding of why we needed to determine the etiology of SL's ankle pain before recommending physical therapy. It sounds pretty obvious, but the insurer has a financial incentive to deny or delay care.

Prior authorization not only detracts from care for the patient who needs it, but it also diverts physician care from other patients. The time that a physician spends writing letters or engaging in a peer to peer is time that other patients in the office are kept waiting. Furthermore, physician offices often have to hire special staff just to address prior authorization issues.

In 2019, the AMA conducted a survey of 1,000 practicing physicians looking at how prior authorization affected their practice.[54] Their findings were notable for the following:

- Physicians complete, on average, 40 prior authorization requests a week, requiring 14.4 hours to complete.
- 86% of physicians report the burden of prior authorization as being high or extremely high.
- 86% feel that the burden has increased over the last five years.
- 43% cite this increase as being significant.
- 91% report that prior authorizations result in delays in patient care.
- 48% describe these delays as occurring often or always.
- 74% of doctors note that patients may actually abandon care because of prior authorization.
- 24% report that prior authorization has led to a serious adverse event in their patients with 16% reporting that prior authorization has resulted in hospitalizations.

Perhaps the most striking finding was that 90% of physicians reported that prior authorization negatively impacts patient care. Interestingly, the issue of prior authorization made national headlines in 2018, when a former medical director for Aetna in California admitted under oath that he never looked at patients' records when deciding whether to approve or deny care.[55,56]

Insurers may also delay care by mandating needless preliminary tests that provide no useful information. Examples include X-rays of the spine when the concern is a herniated disk, or X-rays of a knee when the concern is torn cartilage. In both cases, the X-rays will not reveal the suspected pathology, and an MRI is required. These unnecessary X-rays result in delay of diagnosis and treatment for the patient and wasted money for the third party payer.

Then there is the issue of step therapy. Step therapy dictates that patients must try a "preferred" (less expensive?) drug first, even if the treating physician feels that the drug is less effective or not appropriate in the particular case. Some patients are denied medicine they have taken successfully for years in exchange for a new medicine that they have never taken.

My patient "BC" was a prime example of this. I diagnosed her with psoriatic arthritis in 1995. She was initially treated with sulfasalazine and then methotrexate, which are first-line agents for this condition. She did well with conservative therapy for a few years, but then her illness progressed. She was very fearful about going on stronger medication, but her arthritis needed more aggressive therapy. She started on Remicade in 2001, when her level of pain overcame her fear. She did well at first, but the drug lost efficacy and she was then started on Enbrel in early 2002. She did extremely well with Enbrel and has been on that medication alone for the last 19 years. This medication gave her back her life. We eventually cut her office visits to once a year because she was doing so well.

In 2021, she needed to get prior authorization for Enbrel even though she had been on it successfully for 19 years. The insurer often requires prior authorization periodically to make sure the drug is still needed. I have never been clear as to why an insurer feels that a physician would continue to prescribe a drug if it were no longer needed. I know that they do not want to spend money needlessly, but it speaks to their distrust of the care that physicians provide. The Enbrel was approved without a problem, but later in the year she changed her insurer. This resulted in a new prior authorization request. The new insurer denied Enbrel because she "had not had an inadequate response or inability to tolerate two of the following: Humira, Cimzia, Simponi, Stelara, or Tremfya, followed by an inadequate response or inability to tolerate Orencia, Xeljanz, or Taltz."

All of these medications are other biologics used to treat psoriatic arthritis. They are no better or no worse than Enbrel in treating psoriatic arthritis patients in general, but in this case, BC had already been on Enbrel for 19 years with excellent results. There was no medical rationale to change medications. As per this new insurer, BC needed to fail two other drugs from the first group and then one from the second group before they would approve the drug that had been working well for her for so many years. What could possibly be a valid justification for this decision?

This denial of Enbrel occurred after I had retired, and now one of my former partners, who did not even know BC, had to fight the battle with the insurance company. At first, the insurer would not even allow a peer to peer to discuss this, as they had set a 14-day time limit from the time of denial for a peer to peer. This time period expired. Through the persistence of my staff, my partner was eventually able to do the peer to peer. The initial result was that the insurance doctor said she could not approve it and that it would have to be appealed at a higher level, resulting in further delay. This was bureaucracy piled on top of bureaucracy. Fortunately, my partner was able to ultimately get the Enbrel approved. I must confess that I do not know how she got it done.

How much time was spent by my staff and my partner, and how much anxiety was generated in the patient for her to continue on a medication that had been efficacious and tolerated for 19 years? Insurance decisions like this make no sense to me and are examples of why I am so passionate about the need to reform the prior authorization process.

Sometimes, insurers make decisions that are utterly beyond my comprehension as occurred in my patient "MG." He was a 54-year-old male with ankylosing spondylitis, a form of inflammatory arthritis. He was debilitated by his condition to the point that he was in chronic pain and unable to work. I started him on methotrexate, but he did not tolerate it. We then advanced his regimen to Enbrel. He seemed to improve at first, but ultimately this treatment failed. We planned to go to Remicade instead. His insurer would not cover Remicade, so we then opted to go to Humira. I did not have a problem with this as he had not taken either Remicade or Humira, and there was no way to predict which of these medications would serve him better. He started Humira and had some improvement, but his course sputtered. He had to stop and start the medicine several times for a variety of reasons over the next few months, so it was difficult to determine if the medication was working. I wanted him to take it for a longer period of time to establish whether it would be successful. Then came an insurance change and another prior authorization. The new insurer denied Humira, saying that he needed to have tried an NSAID first, before they would approve Humira. NSAIDs are medications like Advil and Aleve. They are mild anti-inflammatory pain relievers, but they do not address the underlying disease. It would be analogous to having bacterial pneumonia and being told that you cannot have an antibiotic to treat the infection until you have tried Tylenol first. A more striking example might be having a pipe burst in your home and being told that you cannot call a plumber until you have tried a mop.

Addressing this required an 18-minute phone call on my part (Yes, I timed it) to speak with his pharmacy benefits manager to get the medication approved. This was 18 minutes that another patient was kept waiting in the exam room. These are the things that go on behind the scenes that disrupt a physician's schedule and delay patient care.

There are other ridiculous examples of how insurers try to cut corners. The person in our office who submits our precertifications recently informed me of an insurer who denied a prescription for Humira, which is used to treat rheumatoid and other forms of inflammatory arthritis. The recommended dosage is once every two weeks, and if it fails, it can be increased to once a week. In this case, the drug was denied because it was ordered for once every two weeks, which is the proper dosage. The insurer said that it needed to be ordered twice a month in order to be approved. Every two weeks and twice a month are not the same thing. The former results in 26 doses a year, and the latter, in 24 doses a year. The insurance company was willing to approve the drug at an incorrect dosage, but not at the correct dosage. That seemingly subtle difference of two doses a year would save the insurer thousands of dollars as the average retail price for two doses of Humira is $9,233, according to GoodRx.[57]

Then there is the situation regarding Modifier 25. When physicians see patients, we need to communicate to the insurer the extent of the work we have done in order to be reimbursed properly. The level of care is defined by how well we document specific variables, such as how extensive a history we took, how extensive a physical exam we did, and finally, the complexity of the visit. Did the patient have one simple problem to address or did the physician address multiple problems at the visit? Levels range from 1 to 5. Level 1 might be for a simple blood pressure check by a nurse, whereas level 5 would be reserved for a very complicated patient who was evaluated thoroughly. Physician visits typically range from level 3 to 5.

In addition, there may be additional charges if there are special circumstances at a visit. This may consist of an unusually long visit or a special service provided. In that setting, the visit is coded with the use of a modifier to demonstrate to the insurer that there was something extra about the visit. Modifier 25 is used to indicate that a patient received an evaluation and management service on the same day as they had a procedure done.[58]

An example would be a skin biopsy done after a dermatologist noted an unusual mole in a patient who came in to address hair loss. In rheumatology, modifier 25 is used when we aspirate or inject a joint in addition to the routine assessment of a patient's arthritis. In this setting, the insurer would reimburse for the injection as well as for the office visit.

In 2017, Independence Blue Cross (IBC) decided that there was too much usage of this code in the Philadelphia area.[59] They devised a new policy such that if modifier 25 were used, they would pay for the injection, but the reimbursement for the office visit, that is, evaluation and management services, would be cut by 50%. In many cases, half of the charges for the office visit would be greater than the charge for the injection. Physicians would actually be penalized for providing an extra service. They would receive less reimbursement if they did the injection than if they didn't. My practice is very large and we could absorb this hit, but these financial considerations were not immaterial for smaller practices. For solo practices, especially dermatology practices, this could have a significant impact on their revenue and maybe even force some to close. It provided a strong financial disincentive to doing procedures.

Under the new rule, physicians were faced with three alternatives when a patient needed a procedure:

1. They could do the procedure and be penalized for doing so.
2. They could not do the procedure.
3. They could bring the patient back on another day to do the procedure.

The third option would mean a second co-pay for the patient and perhaps another day off from work. It would also remove a time slot from the physician's schedule where another patient might have been seen. IBC compounded the issue by decreeing that if a physician was found to bring a patient back on another day for the sole purpose of doing the procedure, it would be considered a violation of the physician's contract with IBC.

In the midst of this change in policy, "OB" presented to me as a new patient in a satellite office. She was scheduled at 4:15 p.m. for 45 minutes as my last patient of the day. Her case was extremely complicated, and I spent more than an hour and a half with her. We were close to finishing up at nearly 6:00 when she asked if I would also inject her trigger thumb. She also casually mentioned that she sometimes passed out with injections. Given the late hour of the day, my staff had already left the office, and I was alone with her. I knew that if she did pass out, I would need help. I debated the wisdom of injecting her then, versus bringing her back on another day when I would have more support in case she did have an adverse reaction. It was a conflict between patient convenience and patient safety. I opted for the latter. Reimbursement did not play into any of the decision-making because this patient did not have IBC. I was able to make a decision strictly based on the medical merits of the case, which is how it should be.

After she left, however, I asked myself the question: what if her insurance had been IBC? Would this have played any role or have been construed as having any role in my decision-making? I had no idea of what we charged for a visit or for an injection at the time, so it would not have been a conscious thought. Might it have played a role subconsciously? I firmly believe that money should not play any role in my medical decision-making, and it doesn't at a conscious level, but I recognize that I am human.

I later spoke with my billing manager and did the calculations. According to the figures she supplied, the fee for a complicated new IBC patient such as this, including an extra charge for the prolonged visit, would have been $458.21. The reimbursement for the injection would have been $69.43. Thus, by doing the injection on the same day, my office would have received $229.11 (half of the $458.21) + $69.43 for a total of $298.54. I would have been penalized $160 for doing the injection had she been an IBC patient. As I said, in my large practice this would not have made much of a difference financially, but psychologically, I would have been outraged at the thought of being penalized for providing proper care. I wondered how much that would have mattered in my decision-making. It would have raised the question as to whether I would truly be delaying the injection for the proper reasons. Fortunately, none of these mental gymnastics came into play.

This policy is ill-advised for a number of reasons. It creates a conflict of interest for physicians and introduces money into specific patient care. Physicians feel they should be fairly reimbursed for services they provide. They should not be penalized. It displays a basic mistrust of physicians with the assumption that the only reason that physicians do procedures is for the reimbursement. It also demonstrates the unilateral nature of insurance contracts. IBC can make amendments to a policy, but medical practices cannot. IBC can therefore nullify a contract any time they want by putting in an onerous amendment such that the only recourse available to a practice is to negate the entire contract. Like it or leave it!

Needless to say, there was an uproar in the physician community but IBC held strong and maintained their policy. I wrote a letter to one of the medical directors at IBC. I also had an in-person discussion with some of their other medical directors, one of whom was one of the leaders of PAPA 15 years earlier. He was not as supportive of physicians now in this circumstance as he had been previously when he fought for tort reform. PAMED also issued a letter to IBC asking them to reconsider.[60]

IBC refused to budge. They are a private company and are allowed to determine their own policies. They calculated that the storm of protest would eventually die down and they were right. The only alternative for physicians was to withdraw from accepting IBC patients. IBC has a very large market share, which would make this proposition difficult for most practices, including ours, although we did discuss the possibility. IBC knew they had leverage and took advantage of it to the detriment of physicians, and more importantly, patients.

Interestingly, Anthem Blue Cross Blue Shield also had introduced the same policy regarding Modifier 25. With the storm of controversy surrounding it, they ultimately rescinded the policy.[61]

Nonetheless, this is another example of an insurer dictating medical care and harming patients in the process. It reminds me of a puppeteer pulling the strings on a marionette. It is wrong.

Insurers also may utilize other strategies to deny care. Such was the case of "EM." I first met her in 2015. She had a diagnosis of enteropathic arthritis (EPA), which is an inflammatory arthritis seen in patients with Crohn's or Ulcerative Colitis. She was previously treated with Enbrel in 2008 by one of my partners and did extremely well with this drug. She was lost to follow up in our office in 2009 and stopped taking Enbrel because she was doing so well. When I saw her six years later, her arthritis was flaring. It was a rather straightforward medical decision that she needed to resume the Enbrel. When we processed the prior authorization, the insurer denied the drug, stating that its use was experimental/off label in the management of enteropathic arthritis. It was not clear why they were denying it now, when they had approved it previously.

In reviewing her chart, I noted that the patient had initially been treated with Humira in July of 2008. When this failed a few months later, my partner wanted to start her on Enbrel. Even though Enbrel is in the same category of medications as Humira, the insurer denied it at that time on the basis of a diagnosis of EPA. They considered the use of Enbrel even then to be either off label or experimental for this diagnosis. This made no sense to me for a number of reasons. First, there were no biologics approved specifically for EPA at the time, but agents like Enbrel and Humira were used to treat patients who had Crohn's disease without the associated arthritis. Second, the insurer had already approved a very similar drug in Humira without issue. Third, EPA is categorized within a group of arthritic conditions called seronegative spondyloarthropathies. The insurer said that they would approve Enbrel if the patient were labeled with any of these similar forms of arthritis. The insurer was basically telling me that I was not allowed to use a drug off label for this specific diagnosis, regardless of any consideration as to whether the medication was expected to work. It is incumbent upon a physician, not the insurer, to determine if an off-label use of a medication is appropriate, and an insurer should not be able to deny it solely on that basis. Enbrel was not experimental in treating various forms of inflammatory arthritis, as it had been in use for almost 20 years at that time.

I noted that when the insurer would not cover the Enbrel for EPA in 2008, my partner subsequently gave EM a diagnosis of seronegative rheumatoid arthritis (SNRA). SNRA is diagnosed in a patient who clinically has RA, but has negative blood work. With this diagnosis given to her in 2008, Enbrel was approved for EM. SNRA and EPA are similar entities, but there are some differences, including joint distribution, symmetry of joint involvement, the presence of inflammatory bowel disease, and other clinical manifestations. My partner had blurred the distinction to get insurance approval for the medicine that she felt the patient needed.

Six years later, I had an advantage over that physician. I already knew that the medication had worked for EM previously. I was now faced with an ethical dilemma whether to follow the insurer's arbitrary rules regarding diagnosis, even if doing so would be detrimental to this patient. More specifically, I debated whether to call this SNRA, when I felt her true diagnosis was EPA. Would it be considered insurance fraud if I changed the diagnosis? Could I defend the decision to call this SNRA, or would I simply be using this diagnosis to get the medication approved? Once again, an insurer had applied a rigid "guideline" and refused to yield without any regard as to what was best for this patient.

I thought long and hard about how to handle the situation and explored my ethics. My moral value of telling the truth and my obligation to help my patient were in direct conflict with each other. I analyzed whether I should kowtow to the bureaucracy when I knew that medically, she needed to resume Enbrel. There was just no medical rationale for her to try a different drug, but that was what the insurance company was dictating.

I proceeded to review her chart in detail to see if I could support a diagnosis of SNRA, given that she had previously been diagnosed as such. After spending more than an hour on this task, I found that on a number of her visits, she had symmetric involvement of her small joints, which is much more characteristic of RA than EPA. I could now make the argument on this basis that there was enough evidence of SNRA to satisfy the insurer without it weighing on my conscience. I knew that I could readily defend and justify this diagnosis if challenged. I had my staff resubmit the prior authorization using a diagnosis of SNRA. The Enbrel was approved and the patient did extremely well. The prior authorization process for EM involved ten different phone calls (including a peer to peer with a non-rheumatologist) along with 16 different progress notes entered into the chart over a ten-day period documenting the events. That did not include the additional time I spent reviewing EM's chart. All of this needed to be done to satisfy an insurer, so that a patient could be restarted on a medication that she had taken previously with great success.

These kinds of issues occur on a regular basis, where a physician must decide whether to stretch the truth a little in order to take the best possible care of a patient. The inflexible mandates of insurers can put physicians in an awkward position with the potential result of compromised patient care. The case of EM was such an example. I was able to satisfy myself with regard to the alternate diagnosis and get the medication approved, but what if I couldn't? Should a patient's health be jeopardized because their insurer denies a medication that is known to work for them? Should we criticize the physician who bends the rules to help their patient, or is the insurer at fault for creating such stringent rules in the first place? Are the guidelines in place to prevent inappropriate use of medications and protect the public, or are they merely a ruse to limit an insurer's financial responsibility? Finally, who should be responsible for determining the proper use of a medication? Is it the physician who is actually treating the patient, or the insurer who foots the bill? These are difficult questions to answer, with physicians and insurers usually at opposite ends of the spectrum.

The conflict arises because of the distinction between population and individual medicine. Third party payers typically place their focus on population medicine by striving to reduce health-care costs on the whole, while physicians are typically focused on what is best for an individual patient. This is problematic because the needs of an individual patient are often at odds with the needs of society as a whole.

The government and other third party payers over the last few years have begun to promote the concept of "value" in health care. The idea is to reward physicians for providing better value as opposed to providing more volume in terms of services rendered. The idea sounds great, but not so fast. The word "value" is confusing because it means different things to different stakeholders involved in medical care.

What is value? In simplest terms, value is defined as the benefit of care divided by cost. Benefit refers to the quality and quantity of services provided, while cost is self-explanatory. Since benefit is hard to measure, the only way for the government to do so is if physicians provide all kinds of information about the care provided. The result is a system of metrics that physicians are expected to meet, and to demonstrate they have met, through increased documentation requirements. To that end, the government devised MACRA, a 962-page complicated reimbursement system for Medicare patients.[62,63] Typically private insurers will follow Medicare's lead on these types of issues. Reimbursements to physicians are adjusted up or down based on how well they meet certain criteria compared to other physicians. This has caused more of a movement toward corporate-type, assembly-line medicine as physicians check box after box during each office visit to show they are meeting the metrics defined by the government. This is especially concerning because MACRA rewards completion of tasks, such as whether a prescription was sent electronically, over the human qualities of empathy, compassion, listening, and caring. These latter traits are not measurable by any template and therefore cannot be rewarded.

As we analyze this ratio of benefit to cost, we must recognize that the consumer of health care (the patient) and the purchaser of health care (the third party payer) are two different entities. Health care is the only industry where this discrepancy between consumer and purchaser consistently exists. Thus the patient, who seeks increased quality or benefit, and the third party payer, who desires decreased cost, have different definitions of value and how to increase it. The question must be asked: "For whom are we trying to improve value?"

Imagine a situation where you have won a contest and as your prize, you are able to choose any car you want to drive. What kind of car would you choose? Contrast that with a circumstance where you have to choose a car that you will pay for, but a complete stranger will own. Would your choice of vehicles be the same in those two circumstances? It is unlikely. The only way that value can truly be applied is when the consumer and purchaser are the same entity. In that setting, the individual can determine if the benefit they acquire is worth the price they will pay.

This dynamic is true in almost every human circumstance except health care. A consumer who does not purchase a product or service will define value differently than a purchaser who does not consume the product or service. In both cases, the mindset will be different than it would be for an entity that both purchases and consumes the product or service.

Think again about buying a new car. This car is one that you will pay for and you will drive. Every car has four tires, brakes, and a steering wheel. You decide if you want to spend more for a luxury car or less for a cheaper vehicle. You decide if you are willing to pay extra for leather seats as opposed to cloth seats. This is not what happens in health care, however.

We can all agree that we wish to increase "value" in health care. The question is whether we do so by increasing the numerator or by decreasing the denominator in our value fraction. Benefit or quality is enjoyed by an individual patient and is subjective. Cost, on the other hand, is a function of population health. It accrues to an insurer and is objective. Cost can be quantified and is therefore easier to use as a measure of value. This disparity between a focus on benefits versus a focus on cost is only one of the problems with the concept of value.

Another problem is determining what constitutes a benefit. Quality is a nebulous term that is not easily defined or measured. Patient satisfaction surveys, often used by hospitals and insurers, do not measure it. Even patient outcomes do not necessarily equate to the quality of care provided as evidenced by PM, my lupus patient in Chapter 5, who followed me after I joined my new practice. An insurer can look at completion of specific tasks, such as monitoring of HgA1C in people with diabetes, or percentage of patients who get screening mammograms, but are these actually true assessments of quality? How do we measure a physician's diagnostic acumen and treatment strategies?

In addition to the difficulties in defining what constitutes a benefit, we must also think about who derives the benefit. For example, suppose we have two medications to treat a patient's arthritis. Drug A is less expensive and works well for 90% of the population, but it only provides mild benefit for this patient. Drug B is more expensive and only works for 50% of the population, but it works very well for this patient. The decision to use Drug B benefits the patient, but the use of Drug A benefits the insurer. Whose benefit should take priority in determining which of these drugs the patient should receive? Who should decide which medication the patient receives—the patient, the physician, or the third party payer? One of the conflicts here is that physicians are programmed to provide quality for individual patients and are not trained to do cost analyses for populations of patients. Thus, physicians tend to struggle with insurance mandates and decisions based on cost rather than benefit to the individual patient.

Consider a grandmother with severe rheumatoid arthritis. How do we quantify the benefit of a drug that allows her to get down on her knees to play with her grandchildren? What is that worth? If there is an expensive drug that would enable her to do this, should the insurer be obligated to cover the cost? Would it make a difference if the issue in question was whether the drug enabled the patient to return to work as opposed to being on disability?

As a physician treating the patient, my opinion as to what to do may greatly differ from that of the insurance company, which has no personal relationship with the patient. Ultimately, the final decision regarding value is made by whomever is footing the bill, but that evaluation does not usually prioritize the individual patient. If the insurer determines that the cost is not justified, it is the physician who has to inform the patient. How do I explain to the grandmother that her insurer does not feel that the benefit to her as an individual warrants the expense to the insurer? When we consider that the benefit and cost to an individual may be very different from the benefit and cost to a third party payer, the current reliance on "value" becomes rife with controversy.

It has been proposed that patients should have more "skin in the game," such that they have more financial responsibility for the bill. There is some merit to this thought. It is felt that if patients have to pay for a larger portion of their care, they will be more judicious in shopping for their care, and will therefore seek out value more aggressively. To that end, we are seeing coinsurance policies where patients are expected to bear a higher percentage of the costs, rather than the fixed dollar figure of a co-pay. Patient expenses may be even higher if they have a high deductible plan where they are required to meet their deductible before the third party payer contributes to the cost. In that situation, patients play a role in purchasing as well as consuming. They can decide, with their physician's help, whether the potential benefit of a test or treatment warrants their out-of-pocket cost, but they must be given the proper tools to assess value.

The problem that arises with this line of thinking is the lack of transparency in costs. Information regarding the price of a service is usually not readily available. The same MRI that costs $500 at one facility may cost $5,000 at another, and the patient has no way of knowing until after the test is completed. Imagine going into a restaurant and seeing a menu item listed as "market price." Under normal circumstances, you would simply ask the server for the cost. However, if the server is not able or is not willing to disclose the information, how do you decide whether to order that menu item? Patients are faced with decisions like this every day. Transparency regarding health-care costs is vital and is often not evident.

In addition, transparency regarding the details of an insurance policy may not be easily obtainable. Many patients have no idea what their insurance policy covers or what their choices are in insurance policies. Thus, they may have insurance, but still be unable to use it appropriately. Insurers do not necessarily make it easy to understand.

I once discussed the use of a certain medication with the medical director of an insurance company. He told me that all of the information regarding their policy for this medication was on their website. I spent more than 20 minutes looking for it later, without success. If an experienced physician who knows what he is looking for has difficulty accessing the information, how easy will it be for the average patient to find? The rules are always evolving too, such that a medication that is on the insurer's formulary today may be taken off the formulary tomorrow. When that happens, patients like BC may be asked to change medications despite many years of success.

The end result of all of this is one-size-fits-all cookbook medicine with the insurer dictating guidelines that have become mandates, applicable to all situations. This is the underlying basis for prior authorization. The physician must follow the insurer's protocol or spend an inordinate amount of time justifying why they feel that the protocol is inappropriate. The care of the individual patient and the patient-physician relationship suffer as a result.

The government and insurance companies control physicians in this regard by creating hoops for physicians to jump through in order to get tests or treatments paid for. They also do so via reimbursement. More and more, physicians are being reimbursed based on the "value" we provide. As physicians, we are expected by our patients to increase their benefits, that is, to improve their health, while we are simultaneously being pressured by insurance companies to reduce costs for society (the insurer?) as a whole. Unfortunately, physicians are left in the middle, forced to pick and choose between two masters with no way to serve both at the same time. That is where physicians find ourselves in this value debate, and until it is determined whether the needs of the individual patient or the needs of society should predominate, we will be faced with more and more difficult choices on how to provide the best care for our patients. In the end, however, it is the patient who suffers from this dichotomy of care.

What can be done? We cannot eliminate insurance companies completely, given the astronomical costs of health care, but let's think about the role of insurance in the first place.

Typically, the purpose of insurance of any kind is for protection from catastrophic costs. Auto insurance limits our expenditures when we have a serious accident. It does not cover the routine costs of gas or an oil change. Homeowner's insurance protects against the high costs of repairs in case of a flood, a leak, fire, or some other type of damage. It does not cover the costs of painting the house or simple routine maintenance. Why is health insurance different in this regard? Generally speaking, premiums are not being paid for health insurance designed to cover the costs of extreme circumstances. Instead, these are typically prepaid health plans that are expected to cover all medical costs, even those for routine health maintenance. That is a more expensive proposition.

One way to limit the oversight of insurers is to minimize their role in terms of what they pay for, and therefore what they control. There are models of care, most notably Direct Primary Care (DPC),[64,65] where the patient pays the physician directly for routine visits, routine labs, and so on, and insurance is reserved for high-ticket items such as a hospitalization or surgery. Direct Primary Care physicians charge a monthly fee and the costs for their services are greatly reduced with no middlemen coming between doctor and patient. Physicians do not have to spend time complying with insurance coding and documentation requirements and can spend more time with patients. Promotion of the Direct Primary Care model is one means to reduce the control that insurers have over health-care decisions.

Having insurance does not necessarily equate with being able to access care. This is especially an issue for patients with high deductible plans. If a patient cannot afford to pay the deductible, or does not know if they can afford the test or treatment due to lack of cost transparency, having insurance does not benefit them.

One strategy to address the issue of high out-of-pocket costs would be to set a cap on the deductible for a given test or procedure. Insurance premiums would increase, but this would prevent an extreme outlay of cash at one time. As an example, suppose a patient with an $8,000 deductible policy needs an MRI, which costs $2,000. If they cannot afford to shell out $2,000 at one time, they may well decline to get the MRI. Placing an out-of-pocket limit of, say, $500 on that MRI, which would accrue toward that $8,000, might make it more affordable and enable them to get the imaging done. In each case, for every test or procedure, the initial payment up to $500 would go toward the deductible. This might provide greater access to care for patients with high deductibles, while still requiring the patient to be a purchaser.

Also, perhaps patients could be incentivized to seek lower prices for procedures by applying a portion of the savings toward the total cap. Using our example above, if the patient can find a facility that can do the MRI for $1,000 instead of $2,500, a percentage of the $1,500 in savings could be credited toward the $8,000 deductible. Obviously, these potential strategies are only viable if there is price transparency.

Furthermore, education of patients is imperative. Patients need to understand how government and third party mandates may affect the individual care they receive. Insurers must be transparent in terms of issuing policies with easy-to-understand language. Patients need to be aware of the different insurance vehicles available to them and the potential ramifications to their health as well as their pocketbook. This is complicated because in many cases an employer provides the insurance and thus becomes a fourth party. This is yet another circumstance where the consumer (the patient) of a product, in this case the health insurance, and the purchaser (the employer) of the insurance product are different entities and may have different priorities in terms of the benefits and costs of the insurance product.

Along these lines, patients must be able to engage insurers with questions without having to wait on hold for an inordinate amount of time. Some of the responsibility for patient education lies with insurers, but patients also must seek out information and strive to understand their insurance better, through their own research. Patients do need to take more responsibility for their health. Too often, patient control is sacrificed to middlemen in the name of convenience. Automatic refills at pharmacies are an example of this.

Prior authorization is a necessary evil, but it does serve some purpose. Not everyone with run-of-the-mill back pain needs to get an MRI. A general rule of thumb I follow is to ask two questions when ordering a test looking for a specific problem:

1. What will happen if the test is positive?
2. What will happen if the test is negative?

If the answer to both questions is the same, the test is usually not necessary. Consider a patient with knee pain in whom I suspect torn cartilage. If the patient has already decided that even if torn cartilage is present, they will not have surgery to repair it, then the MRI is not appropriate as it will not change management. I refer you back to my patient PM who had peritonitis in Chapter 5. Drawing fluid from her abdomen would not have changed her management, which is why I argued so vehemently with the infectious disease attending.

Having said that, prior authorization must be streamlined so that delays in care are minimized. Denials must have specific rationales. Tests or treatments should not be denied simply because, "This is what the guidelines say." Guidelines should truly be guidelines, rather than mandates to be blindly followed regardless of the circumstances. Peer-to-peer discussion should always involve a physician in the same specialty as the treating physician, so that there is a better understanding of the issue in question. Insurance peers should understand the basis for those guidelines. If a test or treatment is denied, the insurer should offer an appropriate reasonable alternative with a rationale as to why the alternative is preferable as opposed to stating that "some people get better with physical therapy." The role of pharmacy benefit managers in determining formularies must be addressed as well. More on that subject in the next chapter.

Finally, the question must be raised as to whether insurers should be held accountable for the judgments they decree. These companies purposely cloud the issue as to whether their decisions are based on medical or payment criteria. If they are using clinical data obtained from the treating physician to make a decision as to whether to cover a particular test or treatment, and are using words like "medically unnecessary," or "experimental treatment" in their denials, then they are at least in part making a medical decision. These medical decisions should be held to the same level of scrutiny as medical decisions that practicing physicians make every day.

The upshot of this is that when someone owns the football, they get to decide how the game will be played. If the rules are not to their liking, they can simply take their ball and go home. In health care, as long as we are so reliant on third party payers to bear most of the costs of our medical care, they own the football and will therefore dictate the rules. This will be true as long as we accept it without fighting back. It is incumbent upon physicians and patients to do just that.

Chapter 8

The Safe Harbor Exemption

I awaited the verdict. I had just testified on behalf of my patient "MA" before a Medicare administrative judge. It would be several days before I learned her fate.

MA was 65 years old when I first met her in 2009. She had a very complicated medical history which included diabetes, chronic pain, osteoporosis, and significant depression. I was treating her for rheumatoid arthritis, which was quite difficult to manage in the setting of her other medical issues. She had failed first-line therapy, and we decided to advance to a biologic agent. The problem was the price tag. These medications are very costly, and most patients need assistance in some fashion to be able to afford them. Although her insurance "covered" these medications, the co-pays were prohibitively expensive. We did manage to get her assistance from pharmaceutical manufacturers here and there over the years, such that she was able to try several of these agents at times. We met with variable levels of success, but cost remained an ongoing issue. Her course was complicated by the intermittent nature of her treatment and the frequent need to use steroids when her arthritis flared, which posed a problem, given her underlying diabetes and osteoporosis. Steroids are well known to affect both of these conditions adversely, so although they helped her pain, they were not an optimal treatment. Nevertheless, the severity of her arthritis sometimes demanded their use. Furthermore, her depression and chronic pain would wax and wane, often making it difficult to determine the efficacy of the medications used to treat her RA. By 2019, she had tried several different biologics but was unable to continue them, mostly due to finances, even if they afforded her some benefit.

We decided to look into Humira, as she had previously experienced some success with a similar medication in the same class. Her insurer approved the drug, but the co-pay again precluded its use. MA informed me that if she could get a tiering exception for the drug from her insurer, she might be able to afford it and asked if I could make this request to her insurer.

Pharmacy formularies are tiered with drugs ranging from tier 1 to tier 5.[66] Tier 1 drugs are preferred agents from the insurer's perspective and are therefore less costly for patients. Often they are generics. Specialty medications like Humira are typically the highest tier and require the highest co-pays. My staff and I made numerous phone calls to try to sort this out, to no avail. It seemed that every person we spoke with from the insurance company gave us conflicting information or else told us we were in the wrong department and shuttled us to another extension. One person told us that there is no tiering at all for these drugs. Someone else told us that these drugs are all tier 5. A third person told us that there were no tiering exceptions. The bottom line was that I was unable to get an exception for this drug for MA, or even a straight answer. I then asked the insurer what alternative agents would be preferred for a 75-year-old woman who had already failed several agents and was suffering from severe RA. They told me there were no options. They had no contingencies for a patient such as MA. Every biologic was listed as a tier 5 drug except for those drugs that were not even on the formulary. I was told that I had to appeal it to Maximus Federal Services,[67] an independent company hired by the government to handle Medicare Appeals.

I wrote what I felt was a strong letter to them filled with words like "severe pain," and "significantly limited in her ability to function," referring to my patient, along with "unconscionable," and "reprehensible," referring to the insurer's policy. I pointed out that MA was left to suffer from an illness that was eminently treatable. I finished my letter by writing, "I hope that you will overturn the insurer's cruel verdict, so that we can successfully treat MA without her having to decide between treatment and food. It is inexcusable to simply ignore her situation and leave her to suffer without even trying to help her."

My pleas fell on deaf ears. I appealed this in every possible manner without success. Ultimately, a hearing before the aforementioned Medicare administrative judge was offered, and I was able to testify in the hope that someone would finally see fit to help MA. I explained how the insurer had left us with no options, as MA was an elderly patient on a fixed income and every possible choice to treat her arthritis was in the most expensive category, even though they were "covered."

The verdict came a few days later, and it was not favorable to MA. I was left with no good choices for this patient and was forced to manage her with steroids, along with a milder agent that helped her only minimally. The steroids posed a significant risk to her especially because of her underlying diabetes and osteoporosis, but they were inexpensive compared with our other options.

My only other alternative was to prescribe opioids for pain relief, which would also have been problematic in an older patient. Furthermore, neither steroids nor opioids would address the underlying arthritis. The result was that a 75-year-old female was left to suffer. The only medication available to provide her with relief was a cheaper, more dangerous drug. I used the steroids as sparingly as I could, and she muddled along as best she could under the circumstances. With the onset of Covid, and my retirement, she was subsequently lost to follow-up.

This is a classic example of the benefit to an individual patient not justifying the cost to the insurer. I stated in the last chapter that having insurance does not necessarily equate to having access to care. MA's case was a prime example. This is a basic premise that often gets ignored.

Scenarios such as MA's case raise questions like: Why are some drugs preferred by insurers over others? What makes one drug better than another in an insurer's eyes? Is it simply a matter of cost? Does a drug's efficacy matter? Does the treating physician's opinion matter? Why must patients proceed through step therapy where they must try one drug before they can have access to another? This brings us to the subjects of Pharmacy Benefit Managers (PBMs) and Group Purchasing Organizations (GPOs). Let's start with the latter.

GPOs were originally formed in 1910 to act as agents for hospitals to purchase medical products and services.[68,69] They deal exclusively with inpatient purchases and serve to relieve hospitals' administrative burden of negotiating contracts with vendors. GPOs buy medical supplies and medical services such as laundry and food services in bulk, resulting in cheaper prices. Initially, their fees were paid by hospitals to cover administrative expenses, and they were incentivized to seek lower prices. The system worked well and the GPO industry prospered over time, such that by the 1980s there were more than 100 GPOs.

In 1972, Congress passed an Anti-Kickback Statute designed to prohibit the "knowing or willful receipt or payment of fees to induce or reward the purchase of an item or service for which payment may be made under a federal health care program."[69] According to the Department of Health and Human Services Office of the Inspector General (HHS-OIG), the main purpose of the Anti-Kickback

Statute is to protect patients and federal health-care programs, including Medicare, from fraud and abuse by curtailing the corrupting influence of money on health-care decisions.[69,70]

In 1987, Congress created a safe harbor exemption for GPOs, which was implemented in 1991.[71] This was extended to include PBMs in 2003. With passage of this exemption, GPOs were now allowed to receive "administrative fees," that is, kickbacks, from vendors. This encouraged GPOs to favor certain products and certain companies over others based on how much the companies could pay them. It provided for a written agreement stating that administrative fees were to be 3% or less of the purchase price, or otherwise must specify the maximum amount that each vendor would pay. These fees were to be disclosed in writing from each vendor to each customer at least annually and to the Secretary of HHS upon request. HHS-OIG was not required to routinely review or monitor these agreements or disclosures.[69]

Government regulation has been questionable at best. The Government Accountability Office (GAO)[72] is an independent, non-partisan agency that serves as a watchdog for Congress. It examines how taxpayer dollars are spent and provides Congress and federal agencies with objective, fact-based information to help the government save money and work more efficiently.

In 2015, the GAO interviewed the five largest GPOs regarding their activities. Their report revealed that GPOs receive administrative fees, which are almost always based on a percentage of the purchase price of products obtained through GPO contracts. The GPOs reported that these fees, collected from vendors, totaled about $2.3 billion in 2012[69,73] and were the predominant source of funding for GPOs.[69,74] More specifically, the GPOs divulged that these fees accounted for about 92% of their revenue in 2012, with only 3.3% of their revenue coming from member fees charged to hospitals in exchange for membership in the GPO.[69] With such a wide disparity in funding sources, the question must be raised as to who the GPOs actually serve, given that they are primarily paid by the seller, despite their obligation to the buyer.

GPOs are free to pass along some of their revenue to hospitals, but the discounts must be disclosed to Medicare and reflected in the hospital's Medicare/Medicaid cost report. These reports are used to set hospital payment rates for Medicare. Medicare payments could be affected if hospitals do not account for revenue they receive from GPOs. The GAO recommended that the Secretary of HHS determine whether hospitals are appropriately reporting administrative fee revenues on their Medicare cost reports and take steps to address any underreporting. It is not clear if hospitals are reporting this revenue because as per the 2015 GAO report, HHS had not reviewed the data since 2005.[69] It is also noted in the report that while officials from the Federal Trade Commission (FTC) stated that they continued to receive and review complaints each year about GPO contracting practices, in the previous ten years, the FTC had not initiated any enforcement actions directed at GPO conduct.[69]

The safe harbor exemption created a conflict of interest for GPOs and later for PBMs. Since administrative fees are based on a percentage of the purchase price, the higher the cost of the product, the greater the fee paid to the GPO. This provides an incentive for GPOs to seek higher rather than lower prices for products or services as they negotiate with vendors on behalf of the hospitals whose interests they are supposed to serve.

The same issue also applies to Pharmacy Benefit Managers. Whereas GPOs deal with inpatient supplies, PBMs deal exclusively with outpatient pharmaceuticals. PBMs were formed in the 1960s when prescription drugs became a new insurance benefit.[75] Their original role was to help insurance companies manage the pharmaceutical aspects of health care. They negotiated with drug manufacturers and pharmacies and offered value by limiting drug spending. PBMs initially were subject to the same constraints imposed by the Anti-Kickback Statute, but that changed when the safe harbor exemption for PBMs was implemented in 2003. There have been significant concerns since then, especially more recently, as PBMs consolidate with insurers to form large health-care conglomerates. Currently, PBMs determine which drugs will be on an insurer's formulary and how they will be tiered. They receive kickbacks from manufacturers in exchange for increased market share through those insurance formularies. I have alluded to transparency before. It applies here too, as the specifics of contracts between PBMs, health plans, and pharmaceutical companies are not available for review.

There are other issues as well. PBMs and insurance plans instituted contract provisions that prohibited pharmacies from sharing information that might save money for patients. These "gag clauses" subjected pharmacists to penalties if they disclosed information, such as when a prescription drug would cost less if the patient paid for it out of pocket as opposed to using their insurance plan. Fortunately, the Patient Right to Know Act,[76] which banned this practice, was passed in 2018. This legislation prohibits health plans from penalizing pharmacies for sharing pricing information.

The scope of the problem in terms of health-care costs is astonishing. GPOs control buying of more than $300 billion annually of hospital supplies, including drugs, devices, and supplies, for about 5,000 private acute-care hospitals and thousands of non-acute care facilities.[77] One study compared hospital costs of purchasing items through a GPO with the costs of going through an aftermarket broker, whose compensation was not tied to the price of the commodities purchased.[74] The study looked at 8,100 actual hospital transactions of various items and devices at several hospitals. It concluded that after-market purchases could save hospitals 10%–14% in expenses. If we apply that to the previously mentioned $300 billion per year, it amounts to savings in the vicinity of $30–42 billion per year. Some estimates are even higher.[78]

Looking at pharmaceutical costs, a 2015 study[79] done by the Berkeley Research Group assessed the distribution of drug expenditures in the pharmaceutical supply chain. The estimated total net drug expenditures that year was $469 billion. Brand-name manufacturers collected $219 billion (47%), while generic manufacturers realized $108 billion (23%). That leaves about $142 billion (30%) unaccounted for. Most of this money, to the tune of $125 billion, went to supply chain entities such as PBMs and GPOs while other retrospective rebates and fees totaled $17 billion (4%). Thus, out of $469 billion, $142 billion accrued to middlemen. Congress allowed for these kickbacks when they created the safe harbor exemption.

The same study also noted that from 2013 to 2015 the percentage of gross expenditures going to brand-name manufacturers decreased from 41%–39%, while the percentage going to non-manufacturer stakeholders increased from 38%–42%. The authors noted that the largest driver in this trend was the increase in rebates and discounts paid to health plans, PBMs, and government payers by brand-name manufacturers in exchange for preferred market access from insurers via formulary tiers, co-pays, step therapy, prior authorization, and so on.

A follow up to this initial study looked at data from 2016 to 2018. By 2018, total net expenditures had increased to 479 billion while the amount going to supply chain entities increased to 151 billion.

In addition to concerns about drug prices, one of the major concerns of the safe harbor exemption is a shortage of drugs and other supplies. The 2014 GAO report[80] looked at both immediate and underlying causes of drug shortages, as noted in Figure 6.

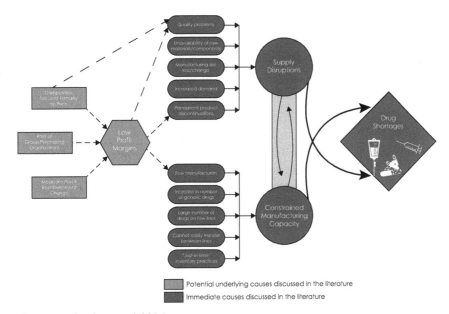

Figure 6. GAO report 2014

Source: GAO analysis based on review of literature

GPOs were included as a potential underlying cause related to decreased profit margins. If a manufacturer cannot afford the administrative fees, they may choose to no longer manufacture the product, which could then contribute to shortages. Furthermore, if profit margins are low, any type of production problem in a manufacturing plant may preclude continued production of the drug. This can lead to sole-source contracting, where only one manufacturer may make a particular product, or one manufacturer has the lion's share of production. If their ability to produce that product then becomes limited due to an acute issue, it can lead to a shortage.

This actually occurred in 2018, when Hurricane Maria damaged Baxter's main processing plant in Puerto Rico.[81] Baxter was responsible for supplying 50% of hospitals in the U.S with saline, and there were only two other companies that made it. These other companies did not have sufficient manufacturing capacity to make up the difference. While the immediate cause of the shortage was reduction in production due to the hurricane, the underlying cause was the extent of reliance on one company for saline production. The GAO report addressed the possible role of GPOs in this, but no conclusions were reached. GPO representatives denied that GPOs played any role, while some manufacturers acknowledged the possibility.

This whole scenario can be explained in an analogy looking at a woman trying to buy a house. The story explains how kickbacks can lead to sole-source contracting, higher prices for drugs and other supplies, and actual shortage of supplies.

Imagine a woman named Mary (**a buyer/hospital**) who decides to purchase a new house (**sterile saline, drugs, or other supplies**). She hires a real estate agent, Kim (**GPO/PBM**) as her agent to help her find and negotiate a good price for said house. She pays Kim $1,000 and tells her that she wants a house in the $300,000 to 400,000 range.

As it turns out, there are five potential neighborhoods (**sellers/suppliers/ manufacturers**), A, B, C, D, and E, which have new houses available in this price range.

Mary is not aware, however, that Kim has requested a 3% "administrative fee" (**kickback**) from each neighborhood before she is willing to show any houses in that neighborhood. Neighborhoods A, B, C, and D are smaller and do not comply. Only neighborhood E agrees to this fee in exchange for Kim showing houses in neighborhood E exclusively (**pay to play**). The Realtor Association (**Congress**), which regulates these transactions, has determined that it is acceptable (**safe harbor exemption for GPOs/PBMs**) for Kim to charge these fees. They reason that otherwise, people like Mary would be unable to afford the services that Kim provides. They declare, however, that Kim must follow certain rules, but as time goes by, there is no evidence that they are overseeing what is going on. In view of this, Kim decides to charge other "advance and marketing" fees (**more kickbacks**), taking the total up to 5% of the sale price, in exchange for her willingness to show houses in neighborhood E exclusively (**sole-source contracting**).

What are the ramifications?

1. Kim is more financially invested in what the seller wants than in pleasing Mary, even though she was hired by Mary. What Mary pays her pales in comparison to how much she is paid by neighborhood E.
2. Therefore, since neighborhood E's administrative fees (**kickbacks**) are the primary source of Kim's income, she will only show houses in neighborhood E (**sole-source contracting**) to Mary and to all of her other clients.

3. Kim will push the $400,000 houses in neighborhood E over the $300,000 houses because her fee (**kickback**) is based on percentage of sale price and $20,000 (**5% of 400,000**) is greater than $15,000 (**5% of 300,000**).

4. Furthermore, there is no incentive for Kim to negotiate the price down on a $400,000 house to help Mary, as this would decrease her own income (**conflict of interest**).

5. Neighborhood E subsequently raises their prices (**rising costs of drugs/ supplies**) on houses by $20,000 to account for Kim's fees, such that those who want to buy a house in neighborhood E now have to pay $420,000 instead of $400,000.

6. Neighborhoods A, B, C, and D (**other sellers/suppliers/manufacturers**) go out of business (**drug/supply shortages**) due to lack of sales because very few people buy houses on their own. Most use Kim, and Kim is only steering people toward neighborhood E.

7. Neighborhood E now has a monopoly on houses sold through Kim (**sole-source contracting**). Supply and demand being what they are, neighborhood E can now raise their prices even further on houses, say up to $450,000 (**rising costs of drugs/supplies**).

8. This results in a housing shortage (**drug and other supply shortages**) because neighborhood E does not have enough homes to accommodate everybody and neighborhoods A, B, C, and D have gone out of business due to lack of sales.

9. Despite the fees charged by Kim, neighborhood E continues to pay her because she generates large amounts of business for them.

The net effect of all of this is that a conflict of interest results in preferential treatment by Kim toward neighborhood E, with a financial disincentive for her to negotiate for lower prices. Her obligation is to Mary, but her allegiance is to neighborhood E (**conflict of interest**). Furthermore, Kim is not motivated financially to show Mary lower-priced houses, as her income is a percentage of the price of the house. This destroys a free market system. The result is higher prices for everyone (**rising costs**) and difficulty in finding houses (**drug shortages**), which is exactly the situation we find ourselves in currently with regard to medical supplies and drugs.

How is this situation resolved? It only happens if the Realtor Association (**Congress**) makes it illegal (**repeal the safe harbor exemption**) for neighborhoods to pay Kim an administrative fee (**kickback**) for preferentially steering clients to their houses. If Kim's income is solely paid by Mary (**no conflict of interest**), she will show Mary houses in all neighborhoods (**restoration of free market competition with increased availability of drugs and other supplies**). Finally, owners of houses will lower their prices to compete for Mary's business (**decreased costs to consumers**).

The controversy regarding GPOs and PBMs is not a recent development and has been the subject of much discussion. There have been four Senate Antitrust Subcommittee hearings[82] and numerous articles written about the potential conflict of interest, including a 2002 New York Times investigative series entitled "Medicine's Middleman."[83] That same year, the GAO assessed whether GPOs consistently save money for their member hospitals.[84] Their report suggested otherwise, noting that "a hospital's use of a GPO contract did not guarantee that the hospital saved money: GPO prices were not always lower and were often higher than prices paid by hospitals negotiating directly with vendors."[85] The conflict of interest was even noted at a November 2017 Federal Trade Commission workshop on competition in the prescription drug marketplace. At the conference, Stephanie Trunk, an attorney who works with a firm that represents the GPO trade group, acknowledged, "The whole idea of the GPO safe harbor is that they are the purchasing agent of the members, and the members are the hospitals. And I do believe that being paid by the suppliers can create a conflict of interest for the GPOs with those members."[68,86]

Throughout this, the main advocacy concern has been for repeal of the safe harbor exemption, which would eliminate the conflict of interest for GPOs and PBMs. Grassroots organizations such as Physicians Against Drug Shortages have been strong leaders in this advocacy effort. According to their website, approximately $230 billion could be saved, $100 billion on the GPO side and $130 billion on the PBM side, if Congress would eliminate the kickbacks that GPOs and PBMs enjoy.[78]

There has, however, been significant pushback on this issue, most notably from the Health Care Supply Chain Association, which represents GPOs. GPOs have maintained that there is enough competition in the market to mitigate the potential conflict of interest.[87]

The American Medical Association (AMA) has been relatively quiet on the issue and has in fact taken a position against repeal of the safe harbor on two separate occasions. In 2016 and 2018, resolutions were submitted at the AMA House of Delegates asking the AMA to support repeal of the Anti-Kickback safe harbor exemption for GPOs and PBMs. I personally submitted the latter. Each was referred to the AMA Board of Trustees which, in both cases, recommended that the resolutions not be adopted.[88,89] It should be noted that the AMA adopted this stance, even though they have otherwise been very vocal in speaking out against rising drug prices and drug shortages.

The AMA board produced detailed reports arguing against repeal of the safe harbor exemption for a variety of reasons, although they did acknowledge the potential for misaligned incentives. They pointed out that GPO contracts are voluntary. They stated that "the elimination of the anti-kickback safe harbor for GPOs would not directly address the drug shortage issue and could create other potential complications in the pharmaceutical market." They cited the 2014 GAO report and commented on the immediate causes of drug shortages but failed to acknowledge that GPOs were listed as a potential underlying contributor to drug shortages. The AMA also wrote that "repeal of the GPO safe harbor could be both ineffective and counterproductive in addressing the identified problem of drug shortages." Their reports further noted that it was AMA policy to pursue a collaborative and evidence-based approach. It was felt that the resolutions contradicted this policy and that repeal of the safe harbor exemption "may not effectively address the underlying issue while simultaneously producing unintended consequences."

The AMA also referenced the disruption that would occur if the safe harbor exemption were repealed and alluded to a "lack of empirical evidence definitively assessing the impact of the vendor fee based funding structure protected under the safe harbor." The AMA pointed to a lack of evidence that the safe harbor exemption poses a problem, but there is also a lack of empirical evidence that GPOs provide cost savings under the current arrangement. This was evidenced by a letter from the GAO to Senator Charles Grassley in 2010.[90] The GAO was only able to identify one peer-reviewed article between January 2004 and October 2009 that proposed savings due to GPOs. The conclusions reached in that one article were that GPOs *can* contain rising health-care costs. There was no conclusion that GPOs *do* contain rising health-care costs. The study was flawed and its conclusions were suspect. Its findings were based solely on the perceptions of hospital directors responsible for purchases of medical supplies. There was no actual empirical analysis demonstrating hospital cost savings.

The AMA went on to say that they promote a collaborative approach. They therefore stated that "Blaming GPOs for the complicated drug shortage problem risks compromising this solution-oriented strategy." They did offer criticism of GPOs with regard to sole-source contracting, but they neglected to make the connection between sole-source contracting and GPOs' funding structure allowed by the safe harbor exemption. They proposed a less adversarial approach rather than stripping the GPOs of "a legal protection vital to their economic model."

The question then becomes, where does the burden of proof lie? Is it incumbent upon critics of the safe harbor exemption to provide definitive evidence that the conflict of interest results in increased costs, or is it incumbent upon proponents of GPOs to demonstrate that the safe harbor serves a purpose and does not affect costs adversely? Thus far, there is no absolute proof of either, although there is certainly a great deal of evidence suggesting the former. I suppose the main question is whether this evidence qualifies as "definitive" evidence. The lack of transparency in GPO contracts makes this a difficult proposition. The AMA has taken the approach that in the absence of such conclusive proof, there is no reason to change the arrangement. Many, myself included, would disagree with that conclusion. It is analogous to seeing smoke coming out of a building. How much definitive proof of fire would you need before you evacuated the building? In this case, there has been a large amount of smoke, strongly suggesting that a fire is present.

I was not pleased with the AMA's decision and I did not understand why they chose to be so conciliatory on this issue. Unfortunately this plays right into the hands of the GPOs and PBMs. Without confrontation, they are free to carry on as usual without having to reveal their contracts. It must be kept in mind that the issue here is not the presence of GPOs and PBMs. The issue is the safe harbor exemption that creates the conflict of interest.

Fortunately, there has been some movement in this area. The Trump administration recognized the problems posed by GPOs and PBMs. Scott Gottlieb, the director of the FDA in 2018, stated:[91]

> Right now, we don't have a truly free market when it comes to drug pricing, and in too many cases, that's driving prices to unaffordable levels for some patients. One of the dynamics I've talked about before that's driving higher and higher list prices, is the system of rebates between payers and manufacturers. And so what if we took on this system directly, by having the federal government reexamine the current safe harbor for drug rebates under the Anti-Kickback Statute? Such a step could help restore some semblance of reality to the relationship between list and negotiated prices, and thereby boost affordability and

competition. But beyond discounting, a web of rules and restrictions—some implemented as a result of industry lobbying—prevent truly market-based pricing and competition.

President Trump himself issued an executive order in July 2020 seeking to eliminate paybacks to middlemen.[92]

More recently, HHS-OIG finalized a rule which would strip PBMs of safe harbor protection.[93] The proposal will take effect in January 2023[94] and will limit some safe harbors, although it will create some new ones.[95] It is also designed to increase transparency as each PBM would be required to annually make disclosures in writing to each health plan with which it contracts. These disclosures would include the services rendered to each manufacturer related to the PBM's arrangements to furnish pharmacy benefit management services to the plan.[96] How this will all play out remains to be seen. It may be an initial step toward addressing the issue or it may simply be a token gesture without any real teeth. Suffice it to say, drug costs and drug and supply shortages have been a huge problem for at least the last 20 years or so.

The bottom line is that pharmaceutical prices continue to escalate, and patients lose access to care as occurred with my patient, MA. Shortages of supplies, medical devices, and drugs persist and as always, the patients are the ones to suffer. Repeal of the safe harbor exemption may not resolve all of the problems, but it would eliminate the current conflict of interest that exists for GPOs and PBMs. Doing so may well help patients who are affected by the tiering systems imposed by PBMs on insurance formularies. Maybe then, the choice of drugs used to treat a patient will be determined by a treating physician based on what is best for the patient, rather than the amount of a kickback to a PBM.

Chapter 9

MOC

It did not seem like a big deal at the time, but once again a seemingly minor detail would change my life significantly and result in a major life decision. I finished my rheumatology fellowship in 1989 and planned to take my board certification exam that year. I had already passed my internal medicine boards in 1986 and had lifetime certification in that field. However, the American Board of Internal Medicine (ABIM), which certifies physicians in internal medicine and all of its subspecialties, including rheumatology, had other plans for me. I did not realize at the time that ABIM only offered exams in rheumatology every other year, and that I would have to wait until 1990 to take the exam. This was merely a minor inconvenience until ABIM dropped a bomb. They announced that starting in 1990, board certification would only be valid for a ten-year period, which meant that I would now have to retake a recertification exam again in 2000, 2010, 2020, and so on, if I wanted to maintain my status as a board-certified rheumatologist. Ironically, if I had chosen to do my rheumatology fellowship immediately following residency, I would have completed it in 1988, taken the boards that year, and had grandfather status, just as I did in internal medicine. I would never have had to take a board exam again. That is not how it played out, however. In the years that followed, I began to realize that board certification, while a very appropriate concept in principle, was a travesty in terms of how it was being implemented.

To understand the concept of board certification, we need to go back to the early 1900s. At that time, medical education was not well standardized. There was a great deal of variation in medical education requirements, training, and physician assessment among medical schools.[97]

The AMA wanted to standardize medical education and therefore created a set of basic precepts to do so. They also sought the assistance of the Carnegie Foundation to help research the subject of medical education. The Carnegie Foundation hired Abraham Flexner to conduct a survey of the 155 medical schools at the time. His report, written in 1910,[98] established a framework for requirements of medical education that placed a greater emphasis on science than had been placed previously. The Flexner Report resulted in the elimination of proprietary schools and transformed the nature and process of medical education in America. It placed a greater emphasis on scientific knowledge and established the biomedical model as the gold standard of medical training.[99] Prior to this, physicians were often trained by apprenticeship, and many had a minimal science background.[100]

In the years that followed, medical science began to advance and physicians were beginning to gain specialty knowledge. This necessitated the formation of specialty boards to verify the training of physicians. The first specialty board, the American Board of Ophthalmic Examinations, was created in 1917[100] to differentiate those who had achieved certain educational standards from those who were not as well trained. It later changed its name to the American Board of Ophthalmology.

The concept of specialization expanded in the ensuing years, and in 1933, the American Board of Medical Specialties (ABMS) was formed at the request of the AMA. Three years later, the AMA in conjunction with the American College of Physicians (ACP) formed the ABIM, whose role was to "certify specialists and establish qualifications with the required examination procedure for such certification."[101]

The ABMS currently consists of 24 independent specialty boards with ABIM being the largest. The goal of these boards is for physicians to demonstrate a level of competence and a mastery of the material necessary to practice medicine by completing an exam at the conclusion of their training. ABMS states on its website that "The mission of the American Board of Medical Specialties (ABMS) is to serve the public and the medical profession by improving the quality of health care through setting professional standards for lifelong certification in partnership with Member Boards."[102] According to ABMS, board certification helps physicians demonstrate their competence and professionalism.[103] ABIM states on its website, "Certification has meant that internists have demonstrated to their peers and to the public that they have the clinical judgment, skills and attitudes essential for the delivery of excellent patient care."[104]

One of the most important disputes is whether the programs in place actually achieve the objectives expressed in the mission statements. My focus in this discussion is on ABIM and what they have done. The information presented may or may not be applicable to other boards within ABMS.

Initially board certification was voluntary, but with the onset of managed care networks and increased consumer awareness, insurers and hospitals desired physicians whom they felt were more qualified.[100] Board-certification status became a distinguishing feature. It was considered a mark of accomplishment, with board-certified doctors felt to be superior to those without the credential. Insurers and hospitals soon required it for credentialing. It no longer was voluntary unless a physician had no affiliation with a hospital or insurer. By the time I completed my internal medicine residency in 1986, board certification was a given. There was never a question of not taking the initial certification exam.

It is necessary to make the distinction between initial certification and recertification. I wholeheartedly embrace the concept of initial certification at the conclusion of training. Recertification, however, has become very controversial. I have serious doubts as to whether board certification actually means what it is purported to mean, and whether the general public actually understands what board certification represents. I also question whether the steep price required to maintain it is justified.

The whole structure of board certification by ABIM changed with the introduction in 1990 of the aforementioned expiration date on a certifying exam. Physicians would no longer have to take only one exam at the completion of training to demonstrate their qualification to practice.

Furthermore, the concept of Maintenance of Certification (MOC) was introduced. Physicians would now have to demonstrate a continued commitment to their education through products provided by ABIM, in addition to passing the newly implemented recertification exam every ten years. Physicians already were obligated to obtain a certain amount of continuing medical education (CME) credits to maintain licensure, but with the onset of MOC, the certifying boards required physicians to also accumulate MOC "points" to maintain their board-certified status. These MOC points were separate from any CME credits required for licensure. The initial mandate was 100 MOC points over a ten-year period. MOC points could be obtained by engaging in learning modules that ABIM would provide for a fee. Any other learning exercise had to be approved by the certifying board to qualify as credit toward MOC. ABIM also introduced a practice improvement module designed to help physicians improve the ways they take care of patients. This could also earn MOC points for a physician.

I firmly believe in the concepts of board certification and lifelong learning for physicians. I agree that having a mechanism in place to validate that physicians are exhibiting due diligence in terms of staying current is appropriate. The idea of physicians demonstrating an ongoing commitment to our profession and our patients is a valuable one. That is not what ABIM has put in place and is not how it has played out.

I took my ten-year recertification exam in 2000 without much complaint. It was a necessary evil. Preparing for the exam took several months and required a review of basic rheumatology, along with rote memorization of obscure information. Much of the material I learned was soon forgotten after the exam, as it was not applicable to day-to-day practice. Nonetheless, I accepted this without much resistance at the time.

I first began to recognize problems with board certification in 2006, when I had to engage in the practice improvement module for ABIM. That exercise consisted of giving my patients a questionnaire devised by ABIM, which asked them to evaluate me as a physician. I then had to review all of the surveys, process their responses as to my deficiencies, and then devise a formal plan to address my inadequacies. The next step was to implement that plan over several months and then distribute another questionnaire to see how successful I was in correcting my weaknesses. Finally, I had to issue a report to ABIM revealing the findings.

It sounds like a very useful idea to provide a physician with feedback on areas where improvement is needed, but the practical application is not so wonderful. In a busy workday seeing patients, physicians do not typically have the luxury of time to process questionnaires to satisfy a third party. It is critical to note that this was not a voluntary choice. It was necessary in order to maintain board certification required by hospitals and insurers. For employed physicians, a failure to complete the task could easily result in their dismissal. It was therefore quite easy to resent the intrusion and added time demands imposed by a certifying board.

Based on my questionnaires, I learned that I was deficient in informing patients of the price of their medications. Otherwise, there were no consistent complaints. It was especially ironic because I had no way of knowing the costs of medicine due to the lack of transparency alluded to in Chapter 7. The *many* hours I spent on this bureaucratic task over several months did not justify the information it provided, and it was my first inkling that the recertification process was not about making better physicians.

I took my next recertification exam in 2010. I was now 53 years old and had been in my practice for 18 years. Medicine had changed dramatically with the onset of new medications to treat rheumatoid arthritis and different algorithms for treating other diseases. While I had to brush up on these things to prepare for the exam, I also had to cram to relearn basic minutiae that were not relevant to what I was seeing in the office. Trying to memorize which rare gene defect causes which rare underlying syndrome was not helpful to me as a physician, nor to my patients, as these were not things that I saw in practice on a regular basis. The memorization of esoteric data was analogous to playing a game of rheumatology Trivial Pursuit. In anticipation of the 2010 exam, I took a board preparation course in another city. The course was essentially worthless despite what I paid for it. It was focused on what I needed to know for the exam, not on what would help me take better care of patients. It is notable that those are two different things. There was also the added expense of staying several nights in a hotel as well as time spent away from my practice.

The expense of recertification should not be underestimated. A 2015 study in the *Annals of Internal Medicine* assessed the cost of ABIM's MOC program.[105] The authors reported that for the average internist, the cost was approximately $23,000 with a range from $17,000 for general internists, up to $40,500 for physicians who specialize in hematology-oncology. Those who are double or triple boarded have much higher costs. These costs did not include the expense of a prep course, hotel stay, or transportation to and from such a course.

Physicians begrudgingly accepted this without complaint until 2014, when ABIM went one step too far by now requiring physicians to accumulate their 100 MOC points in five years rather than ten. They rationalized that education should be a continuous process rather than an exercise that physicians engage in every ten years. This was viewed as a bureaucratic reach at best by those who were willing to give ABIM the benefit of the doubt. Many felt that it was a blatant money grab. This was the straw that finally broke the camel's back and it resulted in a tremendous uproar within the physician community.

There were multiple developments in 2014 and 2015 at a national level. Physicians were quite upset at the new mandates regarding MOC and in the furor that ensued, over 20,000 physicians signed a petition seeking an alternative means of board certification.[106] Paul Teirstein, a well-known cardiologist, and a group of his colleagues began to speak out against the MOC recertification process.[107] They criticized it for being expensive and cited the lack of independent data demonstrating that recertification results in better outcomes.[108,109]

They recognized the importance of initial certification but felt CME adequately served the purpose of maintaining lifelong learning rather than the specific modules and exams pushed by ABIM. To that end, they formed a new certifying board, the National Board of Physicians and Surgeons (NBPAS), in early 2015 as an alternative to ABMS's maintenance-of-certification pathway. As a prerequisite for NBPAS certification, the new board required initial certification by an approved ABMS board. Diplomates achieved this by passing the certification exam offered by ABMS member boards upon completion of their training. After that, the only requirements to maintain certification were maintenance of licensure and completion of the required number of CME hours.[106] Physician fees for participating were also significantly less than what ABMS boards were charging. This new board also became controversial, with some proponents of traditional MOC arguing that CME was not adequate to ensure that physicians were staying current and those opposing it arguing that the MOC demands were excessive, expensive, and strictly proprietary for the certifying boards.

The second development occurred in February of 2015, when ABIM reacted to the outcry by making a rare admission of fault. The president and CEO of ABIM, Dr. Richard Baron, sent a letter to all of their diplomates saying, "We got it wrong and sincerely apologize."[110,111] In response to the widespread criticism, ABIM made some welcome changes to their MOC program. They were now willing to accept CME credits as MOC points toward recertification. They also abandoned the practice improvement module and changed the way that physicians' certification status was reported on their website. They promised to make the internal medicine recertification exam more relevant to the day-to-day practice of medicine. Dr. Baron also vowed that ABIM would be more receptive to the voices of their diplomates. It was a step in the right direction. ABIM denied that their mea culpa had anything to do with the formation of a new certifying board.[111]

In the years that followed, ABIM made further changes. They introduced the Community Insights blog, which created a forum for physicians to offer input into the MOC program. I was very active on this blog and there was very lively discussion on a variety of topics. Ultimately, I began to sense, however, that the blog simply served as a forum for physicians to vent, with ABIM providing nothing more than lip service that they were receptive to the concerns of diplomates. There was very little give-and-take on issues, and I rarely, if ever, got an adequate response to any questions I asked. A simple question such as, "What exactly does the recertification exam assess?" went unanswered on multiple occasions.

In 2018, they addressed concerns regarding the high-stakes ten-year exam, by introducing the Knowledge Check-In as an alternative. This was a shorter two-year assessment that could be taken at home. It was an open-book exam, but there still was a limited amount of time to answer each question. This restricted the value of the open-book feature. While this sounded like an advancement, it simply was the ten-year exam cut into smaller pieces and did not accomplish much. Physicians still needed to spend an inordinate amount of prep time in advance of the exam, now every two years instead of every ten. It continued to be a high-stakes endeavor, with the threat of loss of employment, hospital privileges, and/or insurance credentialing if a physician was unable to pass it. ABIM did lower the stakes some by creating the policy that a physician who failed the Knowledge Check-In could maintain certification by subsequently passing the ten-year exam.

The new exam format and the Community Insights blog were further steps in the right direction, but they were baby steps at most. ABIM has continued to maintain the position that it is their responsibility to supervise the medical profession.

The third development in 2015 occurred shortly after ABIM issued their public apology. *Newsweek* published three articles in March, April, and September of that year addressing ABIM and MOC.[112–114] These articles addressed the controversies and the widespread discontent with ABIM among physicians. They also raised other concerns, mostly related to money and ABIM's financial dealings. These articles speculated that ABIM was making board questions more esoteric with the goal of failing more doctors so that physicians would have to pony up more cash to retake the exam. The articles also addressed the amount of income for ABIM, citing revenue figures of $16 million in 2001, which increased to $55 million by 2013. There were references to high salaries, lavish trips, and a luxury condominium.[115] The author went on to describe accounting irregularities and financial mismanagement. He contended that ABIM had an underlying financial agenda that was the impetus for their actions. As he stated in the third article, "This medical protection racket has made millionaires of ABIM top officers, financed a ritzy condominium, limousines, and first-class travel, all while sucking huge sums of cash out of the health care system."[114]

The backlash from ABIM's change in MOC requirements led to much closer scrutiny. Led by Doctors Charles Cutler and Scott Shapiro, the Pennsylvania Medical Society (PAMED) launched initiatives regarding the need to reform MOC. PAMED then broadened the scope of inquiry by presenting the issue at the annual meeting of the American Medical Association (AMA). There was much discussion at a national level, including investigations into ABIM's financial dealings. Both PAMED and the AMA issued votes of no confidence for the MOC process and devised a set of guidelines for an appropriate MOC process.[116,117] The American College of Rheumatology also joined in on the criticism by issuing a position statement[118] opposing ABIM's MOC requirements, stating its belief that "rheumatologists have lost confidence in the program."[119]

PAMED also had discussions whether to initiate legal action against ABIM. That was a topic of discussion at my very first board meeting in February 2016. It was ultimately decided not to pursue this, as the likelihood of success was felt to be low. The mere fact that PAMED was willing to consider this action was indicative of the level of outrage against ABIM. There were further explorations as to possible corruption on the part of ABIM, which were led by Dr. Westby Fisher, a cardiologist who has spent years investigating the actions of ABIM. The issue continued to percolate, ultimately leading to an antitrust lawsuit against ABIM in 2018.[120] The lawsuit maintained that ABIM provides two products, an initial certification and a maintenance of certification. It argued that these are separate products, but that ABIM illegally ties them together, which forces physicians to either purchase MOC from ABIM or risk losing their board-certified status.[121] It reminds me of the old stereotypical gangster cliché—"That's a nice certification you have there. It would be a shame if anything happened to it."

A major point of contention is whether MOC is "voluntary," as ABIM claims. ABIM has failed to acknowledge that physicians must pass this exam in order to maintain hospital privileges, insurance credentialing, and even their livelihood. ABIM has absolved themselves of any responsibility by stating that MOC should be only one variable in determining credentialing, but have they really pushed that idea to hospitals and insurers? Doing so would only weaken the value they place on their own product. Instead, ABIM has successfully promoted the idea to insurers, hospitals, and the public that being board certified equates to being competent to practice. Regardless of what ABIM might say as to how hospitals and insurers should use MOC, the reality of the situation is that physicians must repeatedly pass this exam to maintain their career. A physician who is not certified is not given privileges or credentialed. ABIM repeatedly chooses to dismiss this reality. Their refusal to acknowledge the mandatory nature of MOC or accept any responsibility makes ABIM complicit, regardless of any excuses to the contrary that they may propagate.

Despite these arguments, the lawsuit was dismissed in 2019, although it was appealed. A final ruling came down earlier in 2021 in favor of ABIM.[122]

Newsweek articles. Alternative boards. Statements of no confidence by medical organizations. Lawsuits. Why has this become such a passionate issue for so many physicians? First we must consider the underlying environment for physicians.

In a Community Insights discussion in 2018, a layperson on the ABIM board expressed the opinion that the vehemence she was seeing from physicians was unfounded. Separate from my confusion as to why a layperson was on that board, I was appalled that she felt she could dictate how I should feel. In my reply, I started by explaining to her that:

> Physicians are thwarted on a daily basis from doing our jobs. Insurance companies dictate the care we can and cannot provide, Government mandates dictate what information we must enter in the chart. We waste time that we do not have to begin with, writing letters of medical necessity and doing peer to peers to get medications, imaging studies, and procedures approved. Employed physicians are told how much time they have to see patients and how many patients they need to see. Electronic records hinder our ability to take care of patients, and have made us glorified data entry operators. None of this has anything specific to do with ABIM, but it serves as a backdrop for our anger toward ABIM.

I went on to explain the deceptive nature of ABIM statements with regard to what the exam measures, pass rates, and the involuntary nature of the exam. These statements, in combination with the discrepancy between their assertions that they want to hear from diplomates and their unwillingness to seriously engage with me regarding input I provided in good faith, were a perfect recipe for vehemence on my part. As I said to her, "I do not like being lied to. It makes me angry."

One of the most upsetting aspects of this matter is the inherent distrust that ABIM has displayed toward physicians. This has been a consistent theme. When I took my ten-year exams in 2000 and 2010, I had to place all my belongings in a locker. I had to ask permission to use the bathroom. There was an overabundance of concern that physicians would cheat if not closely monitored. Even when ABIM offered the Knowledge Check-In as an alternative to the ten-year exam, they insisted on a special camera on a physician's computer to mitigate possible cheating.

ABIM has repeatedly expressed in one form or another the sentiment that without a periodic exam, physicians would not choose to stay current. One leader from ABIM directly expressed this opinion in one of the Community Insights blogs when he wrote that "board prep is the most important driver of medical education." The implication is that if not for MOC, physicians would not seek to further their education on their own or would otherwise game the system. In my discussions with ABIM leadership regarding the use of CME credits as a means toward recertification, one board member posed the question to me, "How do we know that physicians won't simply sign into a CME lecture and then leave the room, thereby getting CME credit for a lecture they did not attend?" In return, I argued that physicians are entrusted with the lives and well-being of our patients, and we face the threat of legal action against us if we deviate from the standard of care. I asked him, "Do you honestly have so little faith in physicians that you believe we are not going to stay current on our own? Do you honestly believe that we have such a complete disregard for our patients and our profession?"

ABIM will not directly say it, but their message is quite clear. They maintain the position that they must protect the public by policing the medical profession. They assert that they must measure physicians' competence and ability to practice medicine. The problem is that their assessment fails to measure these qualities. Frankly, I find it insulting and offensive that ABIM thinks that the only thing that motivates physicians is preparing for their exam.

Over time, I became more and more passionate regarding MOC and it became one of my top advocacy issues. I started in 2015 by directing my thoughts directly to Rich Baron, the embattled CEO of ABIM. He was in the midst of many accusations, especially with regard to greed on the part of ABIM. *Newsweek* even described his name as "Dickensian."[113] I knew Rich from my training many years earlier, when he served as my attending physician while I was a resident. While I have great differences with him philosophically with regard to MOC, I never felt that he was motivated by greed. I wrote this letter in May 2015 expressing my objections to the MOC process:

> Dear Rich,
>
> I trained under you as a resident at MCP more than 30 years ago. I am very familiar with your passion and idealism from those years. However, I must tell you as a practicing rheumatologist and as chairman of the Montgomery County Medical Society,

that there is a great deal wrong with the current MOC program. From your writings, I recognize that you know this already, but please indulge me.

Board exams that measure one's "cramming" ability serve no purpose. Much of the material learned in preparation for an exam is forgotten within a short time. Likewise, questions asked that have zero to do with the day in day out practice of medicine are worthless. Furthermore, I oftentimes find myself playing "read the examiner's mind" as I try to guess at the point that the person who wrote the question is driving at.

Questions such as, "Which of the following is the best answer?" when none of the answers are entirely right are maddening. In addition, the lack of feedback in terms of knowing which questions I answered right and wrong argues against the premise that the exam is an educational tool. Fortunately, ABIM has already abandoned the practice improvement module. Hopefully this will be permanent. When I re-certified in 2010, I spent several months doing a practice module that was completely worthless. It served no purpose other than to make me angry at ABIM for the time and effort I wasted.

The main question I pose is, what is the rationale for all of this? If the goal is to determine that a physician is qualified to practice, we should not be testing their knowledge. We should be assessing their judgment. Admittedly, this is harder to do, but with the internet and numerous other resources, physicians are able to look up anything they do not already know. How does an exam measuring what a physician knows at one instant in time enable ABIM to assess a physician's abilities? The real question should not be what a physician knows at one instant in time, but rather what the physician does with all of the information available to them? How do they use it? That is the true measure of the quality of a physician. Passing a board exam every ten years says absolutely nothing about a physician's ability to take care of patients and therefore I feel that his exam should be abolished.

If the goal is to demonstrate that a physician is staying current, then CME should suffice. An alternative could be completion of modules, i.e., open-book exams with pertinent questions. I should not be playing rheumatology Trivial Pursuit. Either of these alternatives should serve to demonstrate a physician's desire to stay current. Furthermore if there is appropriate feedback on said modules and the questions are relevant, I might actually learn something from the process.

I am well aware of your moral character from our time together many years ago. Unfortunately not everyone has worked with you and the amount of money expended for a program forced upon physicians that most view as useless or of limited value at best, comes across as self-serving.

I know you are aware of these criticisms and suggestions already, but I felt the need to add my two cents to the debate. In fact, I personally find the process so absurd and so onerous that I am very seriously contemplating retirement rather than going through another ABIM cycle.

I would be very happy as a practicing specialist in the community to discuss this further with you if you wish.

I hope you are well,

With best wishes,
Mark Lopatin

Rich did issue a perfunctory response to my letter, in which he maintained ABIM's position. Subsequently, I had the opportunity to speak with him in person when ABIM held a seminar seeking input on its programs from diplomates. During that seminar, he explained that the recertification exam was mostly a formality, with 96% of physicians passing the exam. This was a deceptive statement. He neglected to say that this includes those who failed on the first try and had to take the test more than once. Of course, those physicians had to pay additional fees to maintain their certification. From 2000 to 2014, the pass rate for physicians taking the recertification exam on their first try was 84.9%.[123,124] Rich did not seem to understand the trust issue or why ABIM had such a poor reputation in the physician community. The result was a second letter addressing the issue of trust:

Dear Rich,

Thank you for taking the time to respond. I appreciate your input. There are several problems I see with ABIM (ABMS) which help to explain why your organization is perceived so unfavorably, but the biggest one is ABIM's attitude with regards to MOC. The ABIM is perceived as an unwelcome enforcer who has self-determined that they will police the medical profession. The idea that ABIM must make sure that physicians are competent comes across to physicians, not as serving the public or the medical community, but rather as serving ABIM, especially when there is a significant investment of time, energy, and dollars to comply with a program that physicians did not ask for and are not invested in. The idea of a "secure" exam, whereby a physician must deposit all their belongings in a locker adds to the perception that ABIM feels that physicians cannot be trusted. Furthermore, the general concept that physicians must be tested every ten years, sends the message that physicians, if left to themselves, will not try to stay current. ABIM's concept that they must demonstrate to the public that physicians are knowledgeable, again speaks to the lack of trust that ABIM has in physicians. This big brother mentality does not sit well with physicians, especially in a world of MACRA, MIPS, EHR, and ICD-10. Physicians are overwhelmed with bureaucracy and ABIM adds one more component to this. It appears that ABIM has no concept of what physicians go through. Yes, statements have been made by ABIM acknowledging this, but frankly it comes across as lip service.

Furthermore, statements such as you made at the seminar that 96% of physicians pass the exam are disingenuous and serve to invalidate and alienate physicians. You said that 96% pass the exam but you failed to mention that this may include several attempts. The truth is that only ~85% have passed on the first try at recertification over the last 15 years as per the ABIM website. These physicians who fail the exam, then must go through the rigors and expense of taking it again. You did not even mention that aspect. Based on pass rates for recertification exams, ABIM is essentially saying that more than 10% of physicians are not qualified to practice medicine at a given time. That is outrageous! No wonder the AMA recently gave MOC a vote of no confidence. ABIM gave a vote of no confidence to physicians a long time ago.

For there to be improvement, the first step as I see it is for ABIM to change its approach from that of enforcer to the role of educator. MOC exercises (they should not be assessments) need to have the focus on educating physicians, not on testing to show what they know at a given time, which as I have said before is a worthless concept. As I have said repeatedly, I believe that online exercises should provide references and explanations of answers. The purpose should not be on "passing the exam" but rather on physicians showing due diligence.

It is my humble opinion that unless there is this basic paradigm shift in attitude from ABIM, not just lip service, but a genuine shift in how ABIM perceives its role, ABIM will continue to be perceived by physicians as an organization that exists to serve itself rather than the medical community and the public. It is not just a matter of eliminating the exam (although that would be a good start). It runs much deeper than that. There needs to be a change in the culture. MOC as it currently stands, serves no purpose for the medical community and should be abolished.

I appreciate your taking the time to respond to my letter. It was good to see you again and I hope we can communicate again soon to make this a process that physicians will want to engage in willingly, not because they are forced to, but instead because they see value in it. Unfortunately, that is not the case at this time.

Best wishes,
Mark

I went one step further. It is not enough to simply criticize what is in place. As an advocate, it is important to offer alternatives or potential solutions. I spelled out such an alternative in my third letter to Rich:

Dear Rich,

I am writing to try to help you and the ABIM. ABIM continues to be under a firestorm of controversy regarding MOC. In an attempt to appease those who are critical, ABIM has made some changes to the recertifying exam, changing a ten-year exam to a two-year online, open book, less high-stakes exam. I applaud

ABIM for being receptive but this is not enough. I offer an alternative idea for your consideration.

I would propose that instead of a recertification exam, ABIM produces a recertification exercise. Here's how it would work.

The exercise would consist of 60 questions, ideally cases, to be answered. It would be online and would be open book and be done every two years. Sounds familiar so far. Physicians would have three months to answer the 60 questions. Each question would have references and when a physician completes the exercise and submits their answers, they immediately receive their score, along with all the correct answers and the rationales for those answers. Physicians would merely have to do due diligence by doing the exercise. There would be no pass or fail. MOC status would depend solely on completing these exercises every two years.

This offers a number of significant advantages over the current 10-year and even the newly two-year proposed system.

1. Decreased time and expense: Physicians would not have to cram for an exam. Physicians would no longer have to travel to other cities to take board prep courses. It would mean less time away from patients and family.
2. Increased convenience: Physicians could do this from the comfort of their home on their schedule. Physicians could do a question here and there and actually learn more.
3. This greatly reduces the punitive high-stakes nature of an exam. Physicians would merely have to demonstrate due diligence by participating. No longer would a physician be penalized for having a bad day, due to stress or illness.
4. This is far superior to the current system as an educational tool. In medical school, we learned best by seeing a patient and then reading about the particular illness. This would be the same thing. The physician would read about a case, and then research it using the references listed and perhaps other sources to learn about particular issues relative to the case. This is much better than simply studying at random.

5. Furthermore, by providing feedback on questions answered correctly and incorrectly, physicians would also benefit from an educational standpoint.

6. Improved public perception of ABIM: ABIM would be viewed as providing an educational resource, rather than as an enforcer who does not trust physicians to stay up to date. ABIM could still demonstrate that they are acting to ensure physician competency, but they would be doing so as a teacher rather than as a policeman.

For all of these reasons the idea listed here is superior to what ABIM is doing now. By the way, this is not my design. The American College of Rheumatology already provides an exercise such as this, which is entitled CARE. I see no reason why ABIM could not do something like this.

As I have written before, the current high-stakes exam merely measures a physician's ability to study and their test-taking abilities. It masquerades as a measure of a physician's qualifications to practice and should not be presented to anyone as such. I hope you will consider this idea.

Thank you for your consideration.

Best wishes,
Mark Lopatin

Unfortunately, my direct correspondences with Rich and my vociferous and voluminous correspondences on ABIM's blog site attracted little acknowledgment from ABIM, other than to tell me that my idea for assessment did not meet their standards for validity of testing. There was no engagement as to how my proposal might benefit physicians and the public. Again they emphasized their role as overseers of physicians. Despite their claims to the contrary, their actions indicated that they were not so interested in producing better physicians or improving health care. It seems that the main purpose of ABIM is to maintain its standing as the assessing body.

Nevertheless, it was difficult for them and for ABMS to ignore the widespread criticisms that had engulfed them. ABMS subsequently convened a task force to investigate MOC policies, and I was asked to provide testimony from the perspective of a practicing physician. I traveled to Washington, D.C., to deliver a detailed slide presentation illustrating the problems that MOC presented and how my proposed solution would rectify the problems. These were the same arguments I had made to ABIM over and over. ABMS did not readily accept what I had said, but they did acknowledge in their report that there is a greater need for formative testing as opposed to strictly summative testing. They also acknowledged the need for education as opposed to single point-in-time assessments. Again, another step in the right direction, but one that ABIM seems to have difficulty embracing.

Ultimately however, ABIM has moved one step closer to what I have proposed. They recently abandoned the Knowledge Check-In in exchange for a longitudinal assessment that will take effect in 2022.[125] In this newer assessment, physicians will have five years to answer 500 questions. Physicians will be free to use any resource they want other than asking another physician, and they can do the assessments from home. This is almost identical to what I have been suggesting, with one critical distinction. Unfortunately, the new model still insists upon a limited amount of time to answer each question. Thus, the new model still necessitates extensive time preparing for the exam, despite ABIM's assurances to the contrary. It continues to be another version of the high-stakes exam that so many physicians find objectionable.

I have repeatedly asked ABIM to abandon the four-minute time limit for each question. I maintained that this would provide a better educational experience for physicians as they would have the time to understand the problem at hand more deeply, rather than reading superficially just to get the answer to the question and then moving on. I further pointed out that ABIM would still be protecting the public by verifying due diligence on the part of physicians in terms of staying current. Additionally, I noted that this would greatly reduce the stress associated with the assessment, as physicians would be pretty much assured that if they invested the time, they would be unlikely to fail the exercise. Despite repeated requests, ABIM still insists on a set amount of time to answer each question. Through PAMED, I sent a letter to ABIM as well as to every state medical society, advocating against the time limit. I also have emailed and spoken with ABIM directly on more than one occasion regarding this issue.

In their most recent response, ABIM said that:

> It is important to note you will have four minutes to answer a
> question and, each year, have access to a 30-minute time bank
> you can draw from if you need extra time on a particular question.

> This time allotment per question was derived by analyzing data from previous ABIM exams that allowed physicians to access an external resource. It also aligns with the construct of a longitudinal assessment in that it measures what physicians should know to provide high-quality patient care and emulates the finite time they have to look up information in practice.

Their response borders on the absurd. They laud the 30-minute time bank, but for the 100 questions per year, it only amounts to an extra 18 seconds per question. It is laughable that they believe this is of consequential import. The key phrase in their response, however, is "emulates the finite time physicians have to look up information in practice." I take exception to this analysis.

Consider the case of my patient, "KJ," a 28-year-old female whom I treated for RA. I had tried a variety of agents, and we finally settled on Plaquenil and Actemra. She did very well with these medications, but then her liver tests began to escalate, signifying possible liver damage. My first concern was that this was somehow related to her medications, even though this would have been an atypical side effect for either of them. Nonetheless, we stopped both drugs. Her liver tests remained elevated. I referred her to a gastroenterologist and she ultimately underwent two liver biopsies. His conclusion was that she had autoimmune hepatitis, but there was also consideration of drug-induced hepatitis. He wanted to maintain her on steroids long term, but I had significant reservations with this strategy due to concerns regarding the many potential side effects of prolonged steroid use.

There were multiple questions to be addressed in this complicated case. Could this be residual damage related to her medications? Is this autoimmune in nature? Should we manage a young woman with steroids chronically, despite the risks? If this is in fact, autoimmune hepatitis, should we use an immunosuppressive agent? If so, which one is best suited to address her liver *and* her arthritis, and when should we start it? How quickly should we taper her steroids? None of these were easy questions, and there were no clear-cut answers.

I spent several hours on a Saturday morning researching all of this, analyzing the possibilities, weighing the pros and cons of various options, and finally coming up with a strategy as to how best to treat her. The time I spent reading about this was not finite, as was purported by ABIM. I spent as much time as I needed to get the information I wanted. I was not limited to four minutes. It would not have been possible to address this problem in four minutes, even with a 30-minute time bank as a backup. I therefore disagree with the statement that the longitudinal exam emulates how I care for patients in my practice. It doesn't!

I remain unclear what the exam in its current form actually measures. It does not measure the characteristics of empathy, compassion, or the willingness to take the time needed to help a patient. That time may manifest itself as spending a few hours on a Saturday morning trying to resolve a difficult case. It may manifest itself as taking a special trip to the hospital to reassure a patient. It may manifest as taking the time to write a letter of medical necessity or spending 18 minutes on hold trying to get a medication approved for a patient. How does this exam measure these attributes? Aren't they more important than whether a physician can answer a given question within an allotted time frame? Must my ability to manage time be part of the assessment as well? Is my answer less valuable because I took several hours to obtain it than if I had obtained it within four minutes? That may matter in some specialties where time is critical, such as emergency medicine, surgery, or cardiology, and so on, but rarely in rheumatology. I think that patients would prefer a physician who is willing to invest the time to find solutions to their difficult problems. I also do not think that patients would like the idea that a physician has only four minutes to address their issues. They already complain that we do not spend enough time with them.

Although ABMS and ABIM have taken some steps to address the issue, progress has been slow and painstaking. ABIM in particular has been unyielding in their belief that it is their role to ensure the competence of the medical profession by assessing physicians in one form or another. The mission statement for ABMS says that ABMS strives to improve the quality of health care. ABIM says that they want to show that physicians have demonstrated the "clinical judgment, skills, and attitudes" necessary to practice medicine. The question is whether the products they have in place actually achieve these goals. Does certification improve the quality of health care? There has been no convincing evidence that demonstrates this, although some studies have demonstrated a small reduction in costs.[126] Does ABIM actually show that physicians have demonstrated clinical judgment, skills, and attitudes? I would argue no, for the reasons I have outlined.

I have wondered many times exactly what it means to be board certified. The implication is that a physician who is board certified is competent to practice medicine. The unspoken corollary is that physicians who are not board certified are not qualified. Neither of these assertions are necessarily true.

What are the ramifications of MOC? The most important consideration is how patients are affected. MOC has not been shown to benefit patients and it contributes to physician burnout, which in turn hurts patients. Some physicians actually retire because of the process, which means that a patient must find a new physician and start over. Also, if physicians are spending time memorizing obscure material for the purpose of passing a test, that is time they do not have to read about specific problems which could benefit individual patients, such as KJ.

This is especially a shame because the easy change of removing the time limit per question in the new longitudinal assessment could actually resolve the problem. ABIM could make their product valuable, educational, and acceptable to the medical community. They could still serve the role of ensuring that physicians are staying current without inflicting a high-stakes product on physicians. They could still generate income by making this one change. Thus far, they have adamantly refused to do so. I can only speculate as to why.

MOC is one of my strongest advocacy issues. How much does it matter to me? I am one of the physicians who chose to retire rather than participate again in this meaningless exercise. I was not willing to spend the time and energy preparing for the rheumatology boards for a fourth time. I passed them in 1990, 2000, and 2010 and have been a well-respected rheumatologist in practice for 30 years. I simply did not see how my ability to pass a test in 2020 was an accurate assessment of my qualifications to practice, and I therefore refused to genuflect to ABIM on this issue.

Chapter 10

Scope of Practice

The announcement came in May of 2021. The American Academy of Physician Assistants (AAPA) voted to change the title of physician assistant (PA) to physician associate at their annual meeting. This change in title seems relatively minor and not worthy of much discussion, but that is not the case. The following two reactions I came across on social media exemplify why this decision has such significance.

The first was a TikTok video between a physician assistant and her partner.

He: Why did you become a PA instead of a doctor?

She: I told you, I knew I wanted to become a clinician, but I just didn't want to spend my entire 20s in medical school, residency, so I chose a profession that allowed me to practice medicine with full autonomy and still be able to enjoy my 20s and I did. I got to travel to 30 different countries by the time I was 30.

He: I thought it was commitment issues, that you couldn't pick a specialty.

She: Well yeah, that too. As PAs, we are generalists and we are trained in all fields of medicine so I can work as a PA in primary care and then jump to the ER and jump to ob-gyn and pediatrics and that my friend is the beauty of the profession.

This exchange was very disturbing to me. This is someone who wants to practice medicine but is averse to making the commitment required to do so. She does not want to waste her 20s going to medical school and doing residency. She wants a shortcut. I have serious concerns about her level of commitment to her career and to her patients, given this dialogue. This is someone who sees no problem with jumping from the ER to obstetrics and gynecology (ob-gyn) to pediatrics and feels qualified to see patients in all of these distinctly different disciplines. Her words demonstrate a lack of respect for the importance of appropriate training, and that is worrisome to me. More importantly, it should be worrisome to her patients. I wonder how well she is supervised.

The second response to the AAPA announcement was an Instagram post from a physician assistant who applauded the decision to change the title from physician assistant to physician associate. He wrote:

> The @aapaorg House of Delegates has officially voted to change the title of Physician Assistant to Physician ASSOCIATE. I can't even express how happy this has made me. After years of explaining to patients that I am NOT the doctor's ASSISTANT and that I can practice exactly as the doctor does, I finally have a title that describes my role more appropriately. I am an Associate, a colleague, an equal.
>
> I can tell you that I have never felt like anyone's assistant. I have always felt bigger than that role. Even when I was a Medical Assistant, I felt like I wanted to RUN SHIT and not merely assist. In PA School I ran codes in the ER, I held a beating heart in general surgery. I did entire tummy tucks and breast lifts in Plastics. I performed hysterectomies in Gyn (sic) Surgery. I gave physical exams for adults in Internal Medicine AND kids in Pediatrics. I diagnosed rare skin diseases and performed hair transplant surgeries in Dermatology ... damn it, I've done it ALL.

This is also distressing at a number of levels. This is someone who states that he can practice "*exactly* as the doctor does," despite receiving considerably less training. My first question is whether his bravado is accurate. If so, what hospital allows a PA student to run a code in the emergency room with a patient's life acutely at stake? Where is the physician? How does a PA student do entire tummy tucks and breast lifts and perform hysterectomies, as this person has claimed? As a *student*? Did he do these things without supervision? I suspect that this post simply is an embellishment of what actually happened. If not, there is something seriously wrong here.

I recognize that these responses came from specific individuals and do not represent the entire or even most of the PA community, but they are an indicator of some of the thinking within the PA community, which is why there are such serious concerns. The physician community was greatly alarmed by the AAPA's decision, with statements made by the Pennsylvania Medical Society (PAMED), the American Osteopathic Association (AOA), and the AMA, among others, in opposition to the decision.[127–129] There was great concern that the new title would be confusing to patients. Changing the name from physician assistant to physician associate potentially muddies the waters for patients, as it implies a greater level of training than truly exists.

There is similar thinking within the nurse practitioner (NP) community as well. Language is very important, especially from the standpoint of transparency. For example, some nurse practitioners continue their education to achieve the title of Doctor of Nursing Practice (DNP). They have earned that title and are absolutely entitled to use it, but suppose they enter a patient's room and introduce themselves simply as "doctor." Will the patient know that they are not a medical doctor? Will they take the time to explain the difference, or will they let the patient assume that they are a physician? More concerning is whether certain titles are being promoted to intentionally blur the distinction between levels of training in a further effort by NPs and/or PAs to practice autonomously. PAs and NPs provide valued health care to patients and this should not be denigrated. However, it is critical that patients know the training level of the person attending to them.

This occurred recently at a hospital outside Philadelphia when administrators decided to change their overnight surgical on-call staffing from surgeon hospitalists to physician assistants.[130] In their new business model, the hospital determined that PAs would now be addressing acute surgical issues occurring after hours in the hospital setting, while surgeons would take call from home. The obvious concern here is patient safety, as patients with emergent surgical issues or acute post-op complications would now be immediately tended to by those without the same level of surgical expertise. It is not clear whether these PAs had the training and experience to adequately address emergency post-op issues.

Separate from the training issue are continued concerns with regard to transparency. When a patient is admitted to this hospital, will they know that their overnight coverage is not from an in-house physician? Will individual patients be made aware of this before they schedule elective surgery at this facility? Might that influence their decision to have their surgery there? Should they have a choice in who delivers their care? This last question applies to all patients regardless of the setting, be it in the hospital, an urgent care facility, or a doctor's office. They can only have a choice if there is transparency regarding the credentials of the person tending to them.

Perhaps even more controversial than the physician assistant/physician associate nomenclature is the use of the word "provider," which has come into common use as a catch-all term for anyone who delivers any type of health care, regardless of their role. This word serves to further propel the transition of health care from a human experience to a business enterprise with one-size-fits-all care regardless of who delivers it. As stated by Dr. Hans Dufevelt, the term "medical provider" is "part of the Newspeak of America's industrialized medical machine."[131]

Some have argued that this is merely an issue of ego for physicians. They maintain that physicians are too sensitive, and that we should not worry about titles that others choose to use. I agree that ego is part of the equation. I alluded earlier to the concept that being a physician is part of our identity, when I stated in Chapter 3 that our job or profession is part of the basic nucleus of how we view ourselves. I went to medical school for four years, did residency for three years, and fellowship training for two years. Understandably, it is upsetting to me when someone asserts that my training was unnecessary and that someone with much less training can do the job exactly as well as I can. That is a natural, predictable response. Why wouldn't a physician feel that way? Physicians are human too. Ego is a legitimate component of physicians' displeasure and should not be disparaged. I disagree with those who invalidate that emotion and are critical of physicians by saying we should not feel that way. No one else gets to tell me how I *should* feel.

Having said that, there must be balance when it comes to ego. Too little or too much is not good. I abhor when someone flaunts their title, be it an MD, DO, DNP, or PhD, by insisting on always being addressed as "doctor" under any circumstances. Even in the office, I never presented myself to patients as Dr. Lopatin, nor did I request that I be addressed as such. I always introduced myself by my first and last name. I never corrected a patient who addressed me as Mark. Outside of the office, I never correct anyone who addresses me as "Mr." instead of "Dr." in any type of casual encounter, such as making reservations at a restaurant. I find it offensive when others make it a point to make sure that others know that they are a doctor.

That is a different situation, however, than a third party deliberately denigrating the title with the goal of creating a consumer/seller environment in health care based on an economic construct. Health care is more than a commercial exchange between two individuals. Health care needs to be a personal interaction. Physicians and the patient-physician relationship are being minimized for the purpose of controlling the health-care dollar. We are losing the humanity that needs to be at the center of health care.

The use of the term "provider" feeds into the mindset that health care is merely a financial transaction.[132] That is why I object to its use so vigorously. This runs so much deeper than simply an issue of ego.

I have made the comparison between what has happened in health care with what happened to my beloved Philadelphia Eagles when Chip Kelly became the coach and then general manager of the team.[5] Kelly was a firm believer in his "system." He felt that his players were disposable and easily replaced regardless of their abilities. Because of that, he proceeded to trade away or release some of his most talented players and replace them with less skilled players. Needless to say, without the talent, the team self-destructed, the fans were angered, and it was only after Kelly was replaced that the Eagles were finally able to win the Super Bowl.

This is analogous to the systematic destruction we are seeing in health care, which is based on the similar premise that physicians are disposable and easily replaced, and that it does not really matter who delivers care or what their level of training is. This has manifested in a concerted effort to devalue physicians to achieve other underlying agendas, typically financial in nature.[47] The use of the term "provider" is just one component of that effort.

The choice of words matters a great deal. This is very well described by Doctors Pamela Hartzband and Jerome Groopman in the *New England Journal of Medicine*.[133] Their last sentence is especially powerful:

> The words we use to explain our roles are powerful. They set expectations and shape behavior. This change in the language of medicine has important and deleterious consequences. The relationships between doctors, nurses, or any other medical professionals and the patients they care for are now cast primarily in terms of a commercial transaction. The consumer or customer is the buyer, and the provider is the vendor or seller. To be sure, there is a financial aspect to clinical care. But that is only a small part of a much larger whole, and to people who are sick, it's the least important part. The words "consumer" and "provider" are reductionist; they ignore the essential psychological, spiritual, and humanistic dimensions of the relationship—the aspects that traditionally made medicine a "calling," in which altruism overshadowed personal gain. Furthermore, the term "provider" is deliberately and strikingly generic, designating no specific role or type or level of expertise. Each medical professional—doctor, nurse, physical therapist,

social worker, and more—has specialized training and skills that are not recognized by the all-purpose term "provider," which carries no resonance of professionalism. There is no hint of the role of doctor as teacher with special knowledge to help the patient understand the reasons for their malady and the possible ways of remedying it, no honoring of the work of the nurse as a nurturer with unique expertise whose close care is essential to healing. Rather, the generic term "provider" suggests that doctors and nurses and all other medical professionals are interchangeable. "Provider" also signals that care is fundamentally a prepackaged commodity on a shelf that is "provided" to the "consumer," rather than something personalized and dynamic, crafted by skilled professionals and tailored to the individual patient.

The use of the word "provider" becomes even more controversial when we consider a similar scenario that occurred in Nazi Germany.[134,135] In 1938, Jewish physicians had their medical licenses revoked. They were no longer permitted to call themselves *arzt*, which means medical practitioner or "doctor." Instead, they were forced to use the term *behandler*, which translates to handler or one who provides care. The Nazis used a non-specific term instead of "doctor" as a means of debasing Jewish physicians.

I want to be very clear here. It is not my intent to make any equivalence between the current use of the word "provider" and the atrocities of the Holocaust. I am Jewish. My wife has been a long-time teacher of Holocaust studies. It is not a subject I take lightly. My point is that when Nazi Germany wanted to degrade Jewish physicians, one of the ways they chose to do so was by taking away their title of doctor and using a generic term instead. That specific aspect has relevance to what is happening today.

Given the change in title from physician assistant to physician associate and the negative sentiments expressed regarding the word "provider," I was curious as to the actual definitions of various words related to scope of practice. The online Merriam-Webster dictionary provides the following definitions.[136]

Physician: A person skilled in the art of healing, one educated, clinically experienced, and licensed to practice medicine, a person specially trained in healing human medical disorders.

Provider:	One who provides, a person or company that supplies goods or services.
Health-care provider:	This term is not in the dictionary.
Nurse practitioner:	A registered nurse who is qualified through advanced training to assume some of the duties and responsibilities formerly assumed only by a physician.
Physician assistant:	A person certified to provide basic medical services usually under the supervision of a licensed physician.
Physician associate:	This term is not in the dictionary.

The scope of practice controversy extends well beyond physician assistants and the use of the word "provider." Most of the contention has been centered on the optimal role of nurse practitioners over the years. The subject first arose in the 1980s when four states (Alaska, New Hampshire, Oregon, and Washington) opted to allow full practice authority for NPs with the goal of increasing access to primary care, especially in rural areas.[137] Severe doctor shortages in other mostly rural states resulted in several other states expanding the role of NPs in the 1990s. With the addition of Delaware in August of 2021, 24 states currently allow full practice authority for NPs.[138]

My personal experience with nurse practitioners extends back to when I first joined my rheumatology practice in 1992. I have always worked with at least one NP in my practice since then. More recently, we expanded our practice to include physician assistants as well. Some NPs and PAs have been absolutely superb, others not so good. Even the best ones were not qualified to practice on their own. The NPs and PAs in our practice work up new patients and then present the case to an attending physician, who then also sees the patient and formulates a diagnostic and treatment strategy. The use of NPs and PAs streamlines care in terms of gathering information, which results in saved time for the physician. NPs and PAs would also see my follow-up patients if my schedule would not allow me to see them. If there was anything complicated, or if they had any concerns, they would specifically address the problem with me. If the visit was straightforward, such as for a routine joint injection, they would handle it themselves. We trained the NPs and PAs ourselves and worked closely with them. Therefore, we were confident in our knowledge of their abilities and shortcomings. I knew which NPs and PAs could work relatively independently and which ones required closer supervision. This model has served us extremely well over many years. We work as a team, and this has allowed greater access to medical care for our patients. That is not always how this arrangement works out.

The first experience I had politically with nurse practitioners wanting unsupervised practice occurred at a PAMED political action committee meeting in 2014, when I had the opportunity to speak with a legislator from western Pennsylvania. His district was a rural one, and he was concerned about access to care given the lack of primary care physicians. In Pennsylvania, NPs do not have full practice authority, although there is legislation pending that would grant them this privilege. As of now, they are required to have a collaborative agreement with a physician, with the understanding that the physician will oversee their work. This is what occurs in my practice. Many of the agreements in this rural area were strictly a formality, with the physician failing to provide any supervision for the NPs despite the collaborative agreement. Even so, the NPs had to pay a fee for the collaborative agreement and they understandably objected to this arrangement under the circumstances.

Nurse practitioners in Pennsylvania have pushed for autonomous practice by maintaining that they can alleviate the shortage of primary care in underserved areas. PAMED has consistently been opposed to this idea but recently was willing to compromise on this issue. We supported a pilot program that would allow NPs to practice independently in underserved areas in Pennsylvania. After six years, the program would be assessed in terms of the care provided. This idea was discussed with the Pennsylvania Coalition of Nurse Practitioners and they initially agreed with it. Subsequently, they went back on their word and rejected the proposal, instead seeking nothing less than immediate complete autonomy.[139]

Physicians must accept some fault on this issue. I have spoken with physicians who maintain that there is absolutely no role for nurse practitioners under any circumstance. I strongly disagree with that sentiment. Organized medicine has taken the stance that NPs are valuable members of the health-care team, but they should not practice autonomously. There admittedly has been some hypocrisy from the physician community regarding the need for supervision of nurse practitioners. The problem is that individual physicians are not always willing to legitimately provide oversight. That is the situation described to me by the western Pennsylvania legislator. As physicians, we cannot have it both ways. If physicians insist on collaborative agreements with NPs, we must be willing to provide the direction that we say they require.

Guidance can be especially problematic in the employed physician setting, where a decision to employ nurse practitioners may be made by administrators and then foisted upon the physician. In this situation, the physician is not given a choice regarding collaboration with NPs. Administrators may employ NPs because they are less expensive and then dictate how the physician will manage them. Failure to comply may result in a reprimand or even loss of employment. This is a recipe for resentment and inadequate oversight, which can put the patient at increased risk. My independent practice serves as the ideal model, where the physicians have voluntarily made the decision to utilize and train NPs and PAs and accept the responsibilities to monitor them that come with that decision.

Thus, the legislator made an appropriate argument. If nurse practitioners are already practicing independently in a rural area, why should they have to pay a fee for supervision that is not being provided? It would be better if they were afforded the right to practice without such a collaborative agreement. His argument makes sense, but it is not the entire picture. As with everything in medicine, we must do risk/benefit analysis, and the primary concern must always be patient well-being.

I have already addressed the issue of transparency, but the most important consideration is the difference in the amount and types of training among different professionals. Nurse practitioners typically complete four years of undergraduate schooling to obtain their BSN degree, although that is not the only pathway toward becoming an NP. They then follow this up with one and a half to three years of further education to obtain a master's degree.[140] In addition to classroom hours, NPs must also achieve a minimum of 500 clinical hours of direct patient contact to be eligible to sit for their licensure exam. To put that in perspective, this amounts to eight hours a day for only three months. Some NPs may acquire as many as 1,500 hours,[141,142] but even that is significantly less than what a physician accrues. Some programs offer strictly online courses, which may make it difficult for an NP to achieve meaningful clinical hours. There may be a wide disparity in the clinical experiences as prospective NPs seek whatever preceptorships they can find.[143] The experience of seeing patients in an emergency room for 500 hours is not the same as shadowing a pediatrician or working in a maternal health clinic for 500 hours. An NP's competence will depend on the quality and nature of their clinical hours, but even in the best of circumstances, 500 hours represents minimal exposure.

There are no residency requirements thereafter, although some nurse practitioners may go further in their training to obtain their DNP degree. Once an NP completes the one and a half to three years and passes their certification exam, they are eligible to practice independently in some states. They are not limited to the field in which they obtained their clinical hours. Thus, someone whose 500 hours were in pediatrics may find themselves working independently in an urgent-care facility. Contrary to the opinion of the physician assistant at the beginning of this chapter who lauded the ability to jump from specialty to specialty, these disciplines are distinctly different. Training in one area does not qualify one to take care of patients in a different specialty. An NP, especially one with a new degree, may well be inadequate to take care of patients by themselves. Despite that, depending on what state they live in, they may be able to practice without any oversight.

Physician assistants generally must obtain a bachelor's degree, and many programs require prior experience in health care as a prerequisite.[144] This is usually followed by two years of schooling to obtain a master's degree. Their courses may be similar to those of medical school in terms of subject matter. Their education also includes 2,000 hours in clinical rotations, with an emphasis on primary care. The clinical exposure to patients is more than what is required to become a nurse practitioner but still considerably less than that of a physician. There are no residency requirements.

Compare both of these to physicians, who spend four years in medical school after completing four years of college. The first two years of medical school are spent mostly in the classroom, addressing anatomy, pathology, physiology, pharmacology, and so on. The last two years are spent in clinical clerkships rotating through various specialties. Upon completion of medical school, physicians then proceed to residency training, which typically adds at least three years of education. This is entirely clinical, with a focus on a specific area, such as internal medicine, ob-gyn, or surgery. Family practice residents do receive a more broad-based education in multiple disciplines. Following residency, physicians can choose to spend two or three more years in a fellowship program, such as I did in rheumatology. Physicians typically spend about 15,000 clinical hours by the time they have completed residency. This is at least ten times as many as NPs obtain in their training.

Not only is there a tremendous discrepancy in the *amount* of training between physicians and nurse practitioners, there is also a large difference in the *nature* of the training. NPs are trained under a nursing model.[145] The nursing model takes a holistic view and focuses on the whole person, including the patient's home environment and social support system. Diagnoses are viewed in the context of how the illness will affect the individual, their ability to function, and their support system. NPs are also well-equipped to address health promotion and disease prevention. Nursing-care plans concentrate on the needs of individual patients and may include such considerations as basic hygiene, rehabilitation requirements, dietary guidelines, and overall general comfort measures.[146]

In contrast, the medical model places a priority on understanding the etiology and management of illnesses.[144] Physicians are trained extensively to understand the pathology, biology, and physiology of disease processes. The medical model emphasizes the assessment, diagnosis, and treatment of the underlying disorder more than the nursing model does. Physicians are trained to think critically about the "whys" as opposed to just the "whats." Physician assistants are also trained under this medical model, albeit for a considerably shorter period of time than physicians.

Nursing care and medical care both play an important role in helping patients, but they are different entities. They are not entirely exclusive, however. Nurses do learn about various diseases and their management but nowhere near to the same extent as physicians. Physicians do manage the entire patient, but they may not be as focused on the day-to-day details as nurses are. One model is not better than the other. The two models complement each other. They are not equivalent and they are not interchangeable. This is one reason why it is concerning that NPs trained in a nursing model are seeking to practice medicine without any medical oversight. It is especially problematic when one also considers the difference in clinical hours required to practice. The ability to recognize and treat underlying disease conditions is critical to a patient's health. We should not discount the years of medical education required to do so.

One important consideration is whether a nurse practitioner can do everything that a physician can do. If not, what percentage of what a physician can do, can an NP do? Obviously that would be extremely difficult, if not impossible, to determine. An older study done in 1974 compared two groups of patients.[147] One group received conventional primary care from one of two family physicians working with a conventional nurse. The second group received their first contact care from one of two NPs who were specially trained in a program that stressed clinical judgment. The NPs worked closely with the physicians and were free to totally manage the patient on their own, or request assistance from the physician.

The study showed that in this setting, the care provided to the two groups was equivalent in terms of mortality rates and measurements of physical, social, and emotional function. The conclusion to be drawn is that NPs can provide safe and effective care when working within the setting of physician oversight. It is especially notable that by the end of the study the NPs were able to manage 67% of the patients entirely on their own. That sounds impressive, but it means that in one third of cases, the patient required physician care.

The study was done almost 50 years ago, so it must be taken with a grain of salt, but 67% is not an impressive number. I would guess that the percentage is currently quite a bit higher than that given the subsequent advances in education. I have had nurse practitioners tell me that they can do 85% of what a primary care physician can do. Even if that is true, it is still not adequate. Let's go one step further and say an NP can provide equivalent care to a physician in 90% of patients. That means that the NP is not equipped to provide the same level of care as a physician in one out of every ten patients. A physician may well see 100 patients per week. That means that ten patients per week will receive lesser care if they only see an NP. Multiply that by 50 weeks and we get 500 patients per year per physician who would receive lesser care if seen solely by an NP. My practice has 12 physicians. Multiply 500 patients by 12 physicians and we get 6,000 patients per year who would receive lesser care if seen exclusively by an NP, and that is in my practice alone. Is that an acceptable rate?

Consider an analogy that compares the skills of a nurse practitioner to the fielding skills of a shortstop. It is not appropriate to assess a shortstop's fielding skills based solely on whether the shortstop catches the routine ground balls that are hit directly at them. Most shortstops can do that, just as most NPs can handle the straightforward cases. Sometimes, however, the ball takes a bad hop. Can the shortstop field those balls? More importantly, a good shortstop is defined by their range. Can they effectively field the balls that are not hit directly at them? How far can they go to their right or to their left to make the play? Once they catch the ball, can they make the throw to first base, which would be analogous to making the proper treatment decision? Someone who can catch almost all of the grounders that are hit directly at them is not considered a good fielder if they have limited range or if they cannot throw well. Someone who has played shortstop for 15,000 hours has a much better chance at being a good fielder than someone who has played for only 500–1,500 hours.

Nurse practitioner leadership maintains that the care NPs provide is equal, if not superior, to the care that physicians provide.[148,149] That concept basically asserts that medical school and residency are entirely superfluous. They have promoted five decades of research that profess this equivalence. However, according to Doctors Niran Al-Agba and Rebekah Bernard, "There are no credible scientific studies that support the safety and efficacy of non-physicians practicing without physician supervision. None."[150]

The key phrase here is "without physician supervision." In their book, *Patients at Risk, The Rise of the Nurse Practitioner and Physician Assistant in Healthcare,* Doctors Al-Agba and Bernard describe in detail the many studies that purport to show equivalency and the flaws inherent in them.[151]

Nurse practitioners have further pushed equivalency with the "brains of a doctor, heart of a nurse" advertising campaign. The American Association of Nurse Practitioners (AANP) disavows any knowledge of this by stating that they never conceived nor sponsored "brains of a doctor, heart of a nurse" as a tagline in any advertising campaign or as content in any official social post issued from their organizational social accounts.[152] Nevertheless, this slogan was widespread a few years ago as evidenced by the amount of swag promoting this catchphrase, including T-shirts, bumper stickers, coffee cups, and so on.[153] The implication is clear and the generalization is not particularly fair: Doctors are smart but do not really care about their patients, while NPs are smart and do care about their patients. It should be noted that the difference between NPs and physicians has zero to do with intelligence levels. It has to do only with the amount and type of training. Slogans such as this are self-serving, with the goal of blurring the distinction between the two professions.

As of now, Pennsylvania has legislation pending, which if passed, would allow NPs the privilege of practicing medicine without oversight after spending at least three years and 3,600 hours with a collaborative agreement.[154] There are no criteria specifically regulating those 3,600 hours, only that the NP has satisfied such an arrangement. It is not specified whether those 3,600 hours must include any teaching or mentorship. There is nothing that specifies the level of supervision. It should also be noted that NPs would be required to complete only 30 hours of continuing education over a two-year period, compared with the 100 hours required of physicians, if this legislation passes.

The legislation clearly states that it "confers no authority to practice dentistry, podiatry, optometry, chiropractic, medicine, or surgery." In view of that, one of the key questions, if this legislation passes, is what discipline nurse practitioners would be practicing. Would it be medicine, or would it be advanced nursing? Diagnosis and treatment of disease are medical rather than nursing constructs. Who would oversee them? Should it be the State Board of Medicine (SBOM) or the State Board of Nursing (SBON)? According to the proposed legislation, it would be the SBON. If nurse practitioners are engaging in medical diagnosis and medical treatment, why is it the SBON who would be overseeing them? It seems that NPs want to practice medicine but want to call it advanced nursing. They are not the same. From a medical legal standpoint, one must also ask if NPs would be held to the same standards as a physician.

The issue remains very controversial. Each side of the debate cites data that supports their position, and each discredits arguments from the other side. There are other confounding issues as well. I have already alluded to ego, which applies to both sides of the equation, but there are also significant financial considerations. Corporate entities often seek to hire NPs as opposed to physicians in the interest of cost savings, and therefore have a vested interest in promoting the NP agenda.

As for me, it boils down to an issue of common sense. I simply fail to see how we can equate two disciplines with a compelling disparity in the amounts of training, and in the case of nurse practitioners, a significant discrepancy in the nature of that training.

I have serious concerns regarding the ramifications of legislation that would allow those without a medical license, a medical degree, and medical training to practice medicine. Medical school would become a useless concept. This legislation basically sends a message to me and to other physicians that the years we spent after college were totally unnecessary. If that is the case, perhaps the physician assistant at the beginning of this chapter was on target with her desire to not waste her 20s. As always though, the issue should be about what is best for the patient. Patients absolutely should have the right to decide who they want to take care of them, but there must be complete transparency, and there must be minimum standards. Is it really appropriate for a patient to be taken care of by someone who did not want to waste her 20s on the education required to care for them? Should those with lesser levels of training be afforded the opportunity to care for patients with no oversight? We do not allow paralegals to practice law. Why is medical care different?

I want to conclude this chapter by emphasizing again that nurse practitioners and physician assistants are integral members of the health-care team and serve a vital role in health care, working in concert with physicians. However, they are not physicians,[155] and any movements to equate them with physicians are ill advised with risks that outweigh the potential benefits.

Chapter 11

The AMA, the ACA,
and Grassroots Advocacy

I t is often said that trying to organize physicians is like herding cats, as it is essentially an impossible task. This applies to advocacy as well. Grassroots advocates for health-care reform seem to be at odds with organized medicine, even though they both want the same things. I continue to be very active in both aspects of health-care advocacy with my feet firmly planted in both venues.

My advocacy in organized medicine began when I joined the Montgomery County Medical Society (MCMS) and the Pennsylvania Medical Society (PAMED) in 2002, shortly after my lawsuits were resolved. In 2009, after serving as a board member for six years, I ascended to the presidency of MCMS. I had already established a reputation by that time for being quite outspoken with regard to tort reform. In my installation speech, I acknowledged that I carry my soapbox with me at all times and I am not afraid to stand on it. Even to this day, whenever I am about to launch into yet another tirade about something amiss in health care, I hear my wife's voice in my head telling me to put my soapbox away. She knows how riled up I can get when the subject of health care is brought up.

I served as president of MCMS for a year but did not really understand until very late in my term how to use that role effectively in my advocacy efforts. Subsequently, I served as chairman of the board from 2014 to 2019. That gave me added responsibilities in terms of the path that MCMS would take. As chairman, it became my duty to determine the agenda for meetings and to run those meetings. I also had to handle matters that arose between meetings. It was here that I learned how to better use my position to amplify my messages.

In February 2016, I was appointed to serve on PAMED's board of trustees. I subsequently won an election for that position later that year and won re-election in 2020. Ultimately, I ran for president of PAMED in 2019 but lost a close election. It was absolutely inconceivable to me in 2002 or even as late as 2017 that I would one day run for that office. Despite the loss, I still serve on the board of trustees representing six counties in southeastern Pennsylvania.

My experience in organized medicine has been quite rewarding. I have benefited from my engagement in terms of personal growth, the people I have met, and the relationships I have formed with colleagues and legislators. I have learned that forging those relationships is the core of politics. Without those connections, it is difficult to effect any meaningful change. Organized medicine has provided me with a larger platform and with increased confidence to express my views. It has also afforded me greater credibility in offering opinions and a better understanding of health-care issues and how patients are often adversely affected.

Despite my own positive experience, there has been a great deal of condemnation of organized medicine. The brunt of criticism has been directed at the AMA, but individual state medical societies have also been taken to task, albeit to a lesser degree. I have had limited personal involvement with the AMA, despite my extensive experience with the Pennsylvania Medical Society.

The AMA views itself as the nation's voice for doctors. One question is whether they represent all, or even most physicians. Currently, less than 20% of practicing physicians belong to the AMA.[156,157]

Membership figures are somewhat confusing because not all AMA members are practicing physicians. We can do some calculations based on the AMA's own 2019 report of the Council on Long Range Planning and Development.[158] That report cites a total of 250,253 AMA members. Of these, 22.5% are students, 24.7% are residents or fellows, and 11% are retired or inactive and are therefore not practicing physicians. That means that most AMA members are not actually in active practice. Subtracting these percentages from the total leaves 104,606 practicing physicians who belong to the AMA.

The same report lists the total number of physicians and medical students in the United States as 1,341,682, with 8.1% of them being students, 10.4% residents or fellows, and 11.7% who are retired or inactive. This equates to 936,494 physicians who are actively practicing. Of these physicians, 104,606 are members of the AMA. This translates to 11.2% of practicing physicians who are AMA members. These calculations are based entirely on the AMA's own numbers and demonstrate the general discontent of physicians with the AMA.

The AMA, however, describes steady growth of their numbers over the last ten years with an increase in dues-paying members by 35% during that time frame.[159] It is not clear whether the AMA is an organization in decline or one that is moving toward regaining its prior stature. It depends on whom one chooses to believe. Critics point out that the AMA inflates its membership numbers, as many of the members are medical students, residents, and fellows.[157] They contend that the AMA does not truly represent the interests of physicians in practice.[160]

I have had direct conversations with AMA leadership on whether the AMA represents the interests of physicians. They have expressed the opinion that many people are critical of the AMA without having any idea of what the AMA actually does or how the AMA works. Based on my own experiences, there is some validity to this sentiment. This is especially relevant in terms of discussions regarding the AMA's support of the Affordable Care Act (ACA) in 2010 for which they were roundly maligned. Many physicians expressed displeasure with the AMA at that time, feeling that the AMA had sold them out. We can neither embrace nor condemn the AMA's position on the ACA without a more detailed understanding of the ACA.

As a basic review, the ACA has three main components.[161] The first of these is the idea of guaranteed issue. Under the ACA, insurance companies are not permitted to deny coverage on the basis of a preexisting condition. This benefit, however, cannot exist on its own. If people can get insurance for the same price after they have a medical condition as they can before they have a medical condition, there is no incentive for them to buy insurance until they have a medical problem. Insurance companies would go out of business in that scenario. Thus, the second part of the ACA is the individual mandate, which requires people to purchase insurance even if they are healthy. This helps to bridge the costs of insurance coverage for those who are sick. This aspect of the ACA created tremendous political disagreements. Conservatives strongly protested what they saw as a mandatory tax by an overreaching government. Liberals had no objections to the mandate.

The third part of the ACA are the subsidies required to pay for the program, such that premiums would be more affordable for those who have low incomes. These have resulted in higher taxes and higher insurance premiums for existing policies, which many on the right side of the aisle also found objectionable. This is one of the reasons why Republicans have repeatedly tried so hard to repeal and/or replace the ACA.

The individual mandate was a sticking point for conservatives, and it was subsequently removed in 2019 under the Trump administration.[162] As a result, insurance premiums have risen further, making the costs prohibitive for some individuals. This has also resulted in increased numbers of uninsured people. The ACA has been denounced as a failure on this basis,[163] but this would be an expected result once the individual mandate was removed. The ACA is an all-or-nothing proposition. We can't have it both ways. It is unfair to criticize the individual mandate and then also criticize the resultant increases in costs and number of uninsured patients once that individual mandate is removed. There have also been other criticisms with regard to narrow networks such that patients were not necessarily able to keep their insurance plans or their doctors as was promised by President Obama.[163]

The ACA has provided insurance coverage to millions of people who otherwise would be unable to afford any insurance. It also provides for coverage for young adults up to age 26 on their parents' policy and prevents exclusion of coverage for preexisting conditions. For these reasons, it has been attractive to those on the left.

A number of physicians have raised objections to the ACA unrelated to the conservative/liberal continuum. The first concept to address is that health insurance and access to health care are two different things and should not be confused. That is a concept that I have stated previously. Many have argued that the ACA provides the former but does not improve the latter. Two potential barriers to access to care are the aforementioned narrow networks and the high deductibles associated with some ACA plans. These high deductibles may preclude access to care for low-income Americans even though they have insurance.[164]

Multiple studies have demonstrated, however, that access to care has improved with the ACA.[165-168] Despite that, some have questioned whether the quality of care has been affected by the ACA and have also raised concerns regarding the increased workload and costs on physician practices as a result.[168,169]

There have been additional criticisms of the ACA due to concerns regarding physician reimbursement.[169] Some physicians cite the discrepancy between the 35% increase in reimbursement rates over the last ten years for hospitals compared to 3% for physicians. They also note that provisions in the ACA, regarding patients who do not pay their premiums, are detrimental to physicians. Patients who do not pay premiums lose their coverage at 90 days, but physicians do not get reimbursed for any services they may have provided during that time frame. According to Dr. Joseph Valenti of the Physicians Foundation,[170] this is the reason why two-thirds of physicians do not accept ACA plans.[169] If a majority of physicians do not accept ACA plans, access to care will be further diminished.

There are also general concerns in the physician community regarding the government increasingly inserting itself as a middleman between the patient and the physician, and all that that entails. Finally, there are fears that the ACA is an initial step toward socialized medicine. Physicians who favor a free market system object to this aspect. There are already concerns regarding government and other third party interference into the way we practice medicine. Physicians would like our skills and clinical judgment to be the driving forces for healthcare decisions rather than bureaucratic mandates. There was fear that the ACA would increase the latter. This is another reason why many physicians opposed the AMA's support of the ACA.

However, the issue is not one-sided. There are very mixed opinions regarding the ACA. According to one survey, 53% of Americans view the ACA favorably compared with 34% who do not.[171] A 2014 survey of 2,000 physicians by the Physicians Foundation indicated that 46% of physicians graded the ACA at D or F, while only 25% of physicians gave it an A or B.[172] Not surprisingly, physicians themselves disagreed with the validity of the survey, with those favoring the ACA arguing the survey had no merit, while those who disapproved of the ACA argued that the survey was a legitimate measure.

Thus, the ACA has been quite controversial depending in part on where one stands on the political spectrum, with a number of pros and cons on either side of the debate.[167] Nothing comes for free, however, and the question as always is whether the benefits of the ACA justify the increased costs relative to higher premiums, increased taxes, and the individual mandate.

For all of these reasons, right or wrong, the AMA has been criticized by a significant percentage of physicians for what was perceived as tacit approval of the ACA. Their support was not tacit approval. Instead, it was a qualified endorsement and the AMA did express concerns regarding several aspects of the law.[169] Nonetheless, they were criticized as though they had completely endorsed the ACA, hook, line, and sinker, without any reservations. As a result, AMA membership declined by 5% the year after the ACA was enacted.[169]

Leadership of AMA used this as an example of how physicians were critical of the AMA without knowing all the details regarding their position. The AMA did support the individual mandate, however, and this was strongly opposed by those on the right. The AMA also received criticism from the left because of their support for the nomination of a physician, Tom Price, as Secretary of HHS in 2016, as he was in favor of overturning the ACA.[173] More recently, the AMA has also received criticism from the left because they maintained their opposition to Medicare for All at their 2019 House of Delegates.[174] From a political standpoint, on issues such as the ACA and Medicare for All, doctors from both sides of the aisle have attacked the AMA with the idea that the AMA does not adequately represent their interests.[175]

There have been other less politically motivated criticisms of the AMA as well. I alluded in the introduction to the alpha numeric coding system that physicians are required to use in order to obtain reimbursement from Medicare and private insurers. Coding is a meticulous process in which each aspect of a disease must be spelled out in order to receive proper reimbursement. As an example, the code for one of my patients with gout is M1A.0720. This informs the insurer that the patient has chronic gout of unknown cause in the left foot without any tophi (deposits of uric acid under the skin). For another patient, the proper code is M1A.09X1. This informs the insurer that the patient has chronic gout of unknown cause in many sites, with tophi. Overall, there are more than 240 different diagnostic codes for gout alone, depending on acute versus chronic; etiology; joint involved; left, right, or unspecified side of body; and presence or absence of tophi.[176] It remains unclear to me why a third party needs all of this information as a condition for physician reimbursement.

These Common Procedural Terminology (CPT) codes that must be used are owned by the AMA. They receive royalty fees for their use, which is a significant component of their revenue. Less than 8% of their revenues came from membership fees in 2020,[177] which raises concerns that the AMA's financial considerations do not align with their membership.

Any physician practice that accepts Medicare and other third party payments must use these codes, and their electronic records must be programmed to do so. Only physicians who provide direct care without using insurance companies or accepting Medicare can function without these codes. Critics contend that the AMA's ownership of the codes gives them a vested interest in the insurance model and the resultant bureaucracy that so many physicians detest. The AMA's position on this is that it is better for the AMA to be in control of these codes than another entity. Regardless, this is perceived as a conflict of interest for the AMA by the physicians it is supposed to represent.

Along these lines, there are repeated accusations that decisions made by leadership in organized medicine are based on personal, that is, financial, motives that benefit their leadership rather than practicing physicians.[157,178] I have seen similar criticisms of PAMED leadership by people who cite hidden agendas as the primary motivation for PAMED actions. I cannot personally speak to the AMA issue, but almost all, if not all, of the attacks that have been leveled at PAMED leadership are unsubstantiated, with little if any evidence to support the accusations.

Physicians also are critical of the AMA for moving too slowly on issues. As a large organization, it can take time for them to adopt a particular position or strategy. The comparison has been made to that of a large luxury liner that has all the amenities but cannot turn in the water very quickly. Contrast this with the description of grassroots advocacy as a dinghy, which is much smaller and much less powerful, but also much more nimble.

For example, the AMA has taken a strong position in opposition to MOC, but this did not happen right away. It was not until leadership of PAMED brought the issue to their attention over and over again that they took a public stance on MOC. They still are not on board with regard to PBMs and the kickbacks they receive, even though it was initially brought to their attention three years ago. I can only hope that someday they will address this as a concern. They do recognize and promote the need for lower drug prices but have not been willing to speak out against the role that GPOs and PBMs play in drug prices and drug shortages. I have been critical of the AMA on this issue and question why they have been so conciliatory.

Another area where physicians feel that the AMA has failed them was in their lobbying regarding the sustainable growth rate (SGR). The SGR was a payment method by which the Center for Medicare and Medicaid Services (CMS) could control government spending on physician services.[179] The Medicare fee schedule was to be adjusted each year, depending on the previous year's expenditures compared to the target growth rate.[180] If the growth in volume of services exceeded the target, physicians' fees were to be reduced to bring spending in line with the target.[181] In 2001, Congress issued a 4.4% decrease in reimbursement rates, which was very unpopular with physicians. Due to this, Congress was reluctant to implement any further pay cuts in the years that followed, even if the SGR in a given year called for a pay cut. Rather than definitively correct the SGR system, Congress continued to kick the can down the road with short-term patches to override the formula each year until the situation became untenable.

The issue snowballed to such an extent that by 2015, physicians would have been mandated to take a pay cut of more than 21%.[181] The SGR needed to be retired, and the AMA lobbied vigorously for its repeal. So far, so good.

In 2015, CMS opted to finally get rid of the sustainable growth rate, which in and of itself was a good thing that many physicians were clamoring for. However, it was replaced by a far-reaching package of reforms, the MACRA/MIPs program, which created an overload of bureaucracy for physicians.[62,63] As described in Chapter 7, this program was designed to reward "value" over volume.[182] It was presented in a 962-page document that was extremely complex.[183] It was unreasonable to expect physicians to understand and comply with all the nuances. Physicians were now required to meet certain "metrics" that were deemed to constitute good medical care. Once again, the problem became how to measure "value" and determine what outcome measures should be used. There were cookbook recipes for how to provide care, and MACRA demanded an overload of documentation on physicians' parts to demonstrate they were meeting those metrics. If the documentation was not deemed adequate, a physician's Medicare reimbursement was reduced.

Furthermore, the legislation would be next to impossible for small practices to follow, and many were expected to take a significant loss in revenue as a result. There were great fears regarding the further corporatization of health care with smaller practices being bought out by larger entities.[184]

Although the AMA did in fact express concerns over the implementation and various facets of MACRA,[185,186] the general sentiment among physicians was that the AMA wholeheartedly approved of this new model. Physicians were pleased to be rid of the SGR, but many condemned the AMA for what they saw as support for this new bureaucratic nightmare. This is illustrated by the comments of one physician who stated, "All of these people making rules have no understanding of the practice of medicine and the AMA and other lobby organizations for doctors are just as much to blame."[187]

Some of the displeasure with the AMA on these issues is justified but not all. Physicians strongly wanted the AMA to push for repeal of the SGR, and when the new model was enacted, the AMA was criticized for that as well.

I also struggle with attacks on organized medicine that rely on the underlying belief that organized medicine has more power than it actually does. Many people are critical without realizing how limited the AMA and PAMED are. I have personally seen this, especially at the state level. Organized medicine just does not have the ability to change policies of private companies. The AMA cannot force ABIM to change their implementation of MOC. PAMED cannot compel private insurers to change how they handle prior authorization. Medical societies do not control the legislature on items like caps on non-economic damages or scope of practice. Nonetheless, people are often quick to find fault with organized medicine when desired change does not occur.

Some physicians are quite vocal in expressing the view that the AMA and at a state level, PAMED, should be doing more than simply adopting positions on issues that adversely affect physicians. The feeling is that organized medicine should lobby more aggressively to influence those who have the power to make these kinds of decisions and should be pushing legislative and legal remedies more forcefully. In some cases, I agree with this idea but not always. Of course, for a number of people, the motives of large organizations are routinely questioned and no matter what the AMA or PAMED does, it is either wrong or not enough. They "should" have done more.

Thus, there are widely disparate views on what the AMA does and what people feel it should do. Many physicians feel that it does not represent them, and grassroots advocacy has flourished as a result.

I did not truly get started in grassroots advocacy until 2015, despite my previous experiences with PAPA more than ten years earlier. I had not yet served in organized medicine at the state level by 2015, but I was fairly well established in a leadership role at the county level. Despite that, I was pretty much clueless (yet again) as to the world of grassroots advocacy. That changed when I met Marion Mass in April of that year. A local newspaper was interviewing a group of physicians for a story on health care, and she and I met at that meeting. There is no way I can tell the story of my evolution as a health-care advocate without including her. She has been a mentor, a colleague, and a trusted friend who has turned the volume up multiple notches on my advocacy efforts as well as the advocacy efforts of others. It was she who introduced me to grassroots advocacy.

Marion is a pediatrician who was in private practice in the suburbs of Philadelphia at the time I met her. In the following two years she became nationally known as a health-care advocate and one of the founders of Practicing Physicians of America,[188] (PPA). PPA is a national grassroots advocacy group focused on empowering physicians in the health-care environment on issues such as MOC and PBMs. She has access to numerous legislators at both a local and national level with many of their phone numbers on speed dial.

I had already been advocating for more than ten years by the time I met her, but I had not yet learned the power of social media. Although I joined Facebook in 2009, I rarely used it and did not join Twitter until 2016. I had a very limited social media presence before I met her.

Through Marion, I become involved with grassroots advocacy groups such as Physicians Working Together (PWT),[189] Physicians Against Drug Shortages (PADS),[190] and Physicians for Patient Protection (PPP),[191] as well as others. I was invited to Washington, D.C., to join the National Physicians Council for Healthcare Policy through Marion's connections with Congressman Pete Sessions. It was here that I first met Bob Campbell, an anesthesiologist who educated me on GPOs and PBMs and their effects on health care. I met other dedicated physician advocates from across the country who sacrificed their time and money to attend meetings in Washington, D.C., with the goal of improving our health-care system. I made new acquaintances and formed new friendships. My social media presence increased dramatically and my Facebook page and Twitter feed soon were filled with political statements and commentary regarding various health-care issues. My confidence level grew as my opinions were liked, discussed, shared, and retweeted. My phone contact list, my email address book, and my Facebook friend list all expanded accordingly.

As I became more facile in grassroots advocacy, a game changer occurred in February 2016. I was in Washington, D.C., for a PAMED political action committee retreat that was being held in conjunction with the yearly AMA advocacy meeting. I had never attended one of their advocacy meetings and was not sure what to expect. I already had mixed feelings about the AMA as expressed earlier.

I was pleasantly surprised by what I saw. Many of the same issues that I had been hearing about at a grassroots level, such as prior authorization, scope of practice, MOC, and documentation requirements were being addressed at the advocacy conference. Seeing the agenda, I wondered why so many at a grassroots level were so cynical of the AMA. I began to think that since the AMA and grassroots activists are fighting the same battles, why not have a meeting of the minds? I came up with the idea that perhaps the two groups could somehow pool their resources together in a joint effort.

To that end, I approached Andy Gurman who was the incoming president of the AMA and also a Pennsylvania physician. I knew who he was from PAMED meetings, but I did not know him personally. Nonetheless, not knowing someone was not about to stop me from approaching them. I explained to him how grassroots organizations were at odds with the AMA, despite having very similar agendas. I reasoned that it might be productive to have a meeting between leadership of the AMA and leaders of these organizations to discuss ways in which they could work together. Andy was very gracious and agreed to a one-hour meeting at the AMA annual meeting in November. I cannot imagine how busy the president of the AMA must be, and how many people must want him for this and that, but even though he did not know me, he set an hour aside for my proposed meeting. Now all I had to do was convince leadership of grassroots organizations to fly to Orlando for a one-hour meeting.

I spent many hours on social media laying out the situation and seeking people to attend. There were more than 100 emails back and forth discussing the rare opportunity. Some were very supportive of the idea. Some objected strenuously, with advice not to meet with the AMA under any circumstances. One physician wrote, "The AMA has been complicit in the decline of medicine for the past 20 years and has positioned itself to financially benefit from the bureaucratization of medicine in the United States." The previously noted criticisms of the AMA's support for the ACA and MACRA for their own purposes were also freely expressed.

Ultimately, leaders of PWT, the Benjamin Rush Institute (BRI), Let My Doctor Practice, Doctors for Patient Care, and the Association of Independent Doctors (AID) attended. We had dinner together in Disney World the night before the AMA meeting. I again formed new connections that would serve me later. I described earlier in this book how relationships are crucial to politics. They are also important in the area of advocacy. We shared personal stories and discussed various concerns in health care in preparation for the meeting with the AMA the next day.

The meeting ultimately proved to be a disappointment. The AMA was very willing to have members of grassroots organizations join them. They were not so willing to meet halfway or even part of the way. They noted that they have the vast infrastructure required to move forward that grassroots groups do not. This meeting is where the analogy of the AMA as a luxury ocean liner came from, with grassroots organizations described as dinghies. Because it is such a large organization, the AMA has power, but it does not have the nimbleness that smaller organizations do. Unfortunately, the meeting did not bring grassroots leaders and the AMA any closer together as I had hoped it would.

What the meeting did accomplish, however, was that it served to bring leaders of grassroots organizations closer together. Marion had already been conducting a series of monthly phone conferences between various grassroots leaders, and this meeting served to enhance existing relationships. Over the next few years, networks between advocacy groups continued to evolve.

This ultimately led to the formation of Free2Care, a coalition of grassroots organizations including PWT, BRI, and AID, all of which were in attendance at the AMA meeting I organized.

Free2Care's main focus is on the patient-physician relationship.[192] They were an expansion of PPA, and PPA is one of their member organizations. Their basic tenets are that:

1. Health care is fundamentally about the patient-physician relationship.
2. Health care can be transformed through price transparency, access, and choice.
3. Health care is personal, not partisan.

They have spoken to many of the issues addressed in this book, and see themselves as an alternative to the AMA. They describe their organization as follows:

> Free2Care is a non-partisan coalition of patient and physician advocacy groups around the nation. Our membership of over 8 million people inclusive of over 72,000 physicians believe in what the AMA does not, the doctor/patient relationship. Policing the speech of dissenting physicians from their clearly partisan agenda will further hurt relationships with patients and perhaps worse, the practice of medicine itself.[193]

Their inaugural meeting took place in April 2019. Just as with PPA, Marion also played an instrumental role in seeing this group come to fruition. Free2Care subsequently produced a white paper written by grassroots leaders from across the nation on how to reduce cost and waste in American medicine.[194] The white paper was focused on health-care solutions and was described as a physician-led road map to patient-centered medical care. I was out of the country when this meeting took place and was therefore unable to attend, but I was honored to be asked to write the section on prior authorization for the follow-up white paper in the fall of 2021.

The formation and growth of this organization are astonishing and illustrate the power of grassroots advocacy and social media. The 72,000 physician members represent more than two-thirds of the approximately 105,000 practicing physicians who are AMA members.[158] It should be noted that Free2Care has only been around for two years, while the AMA was founded in 1847.

I have had the opportunity to work with Marion on other grassroots endeavors. One of the most prominent was health-care town halls. The nucleus of the idea first originated in 2009 when I sought a way for physicians to make a statement regarding all that was wrong in health care. At the time the focus was still on tort reform and defensive medicine. I had the idea of every physician closing their offices, except for emergency care, for one day just before the November elections the following year. I envisioned this one day, entitled "Patients' First Day," as the culmination of a media blitz designed to raise public awareness of the issues that compromise health care. One of the main goals was to ask the public, "Do you know where your legislator stands on important issues such as tort reform and defensive medicine that affect your ability to obtain medical care?" I wanted to send a message to legislators on the importance of these issues. I anticipated rallies and health fairs as a means of education. I created a detailed proposal as to how we could use this day to educate the public about health issues and inform them where legislators stood on the issues that affect their access to care.

I formally submitted the idea to PAMED leadership, but it was rejected due to concerns regarding accusations of collusion if all physicians chose the same day to close their offices. I felt that it would make a strong statement but had no way to implement it on my own.

The idea lay dormant until 2016 when I discussed it with Marion. Together, we resurrected the idea and submitted another proposal to PAMED. We included the ideas of panel discussions and town halls as a means to educate patients. This time, however, there was also grassroots support for the proposal. We had the opportunity to discuss the idea in person with several leaders who happened to be in Philadelphia in June of that year. PAMED turned us down again, and that was where the idea of holding health-care town halls as an alternative gained momentum. These would not require the presence of a large organization to implement and are an example of the nimbleness I described earlier.

Health-care town halls were public seminars designed to educate patients. They consisted of practicing physicians discussing the topics that directly affect the care that patients receive. Marion and I enlisted the help of Dr. Jay Rothkopf, who was president of the Montgomery County Medical Society at the time. We had no budget to use for advertising and could only promote the events by word of mouth and social media. The *Philadelphia Inquirer* was kind enough to publish my op-ed regarding these events, and we held our first two town halls, one in Montgomery County and one in Philadelphia, in October of 2016. The first was quite successful. The latter was less well attended, as it was held on the same night as one of the Trump-Clinton debates. More importantly, however, the idea was picked up by Dr. Kim Jackson of Physicians Working Together. Health-care town halls went national. We created a template for the event in terms of topics, publicity, and the actual logistics. Physicians from multiple states then held their own town halls through PWT, with the goal of educating the public as to what really goes on in health care. Marion and I subsequently ran another town hall at my synagogue, but our most publicized town hall was held in 2018 under the auspices of AMAC, the Association of Mature American Citizens. These town halls are a prototype for what we need to do, which is to educate our patients about the many forces in health care that compromise the relationship they have with their physician and the care they receive. Education comes slowly, however, and the message needs to be repeated over and over and over again.

It was also through Marion that I was asked to speak at the Library of Congress on the use of social media in grassroots advocacy. I found that quite ironic since I had only been advocating on social media for two years at the time. She was organizing the kickoff event for PPA in 2017 and was able to obtain the venue through our mutual congressman, Brian Fitzpatrick. I was initially asked to speak on MOC, but that honor was given to Wes Fisher when he became available. Wes may well be the country's foremost expert on MOC and ABIM. I had the opportunity to meet him in person for the first time there, and we have communicated numerous times on social media since then regarding the problems associated with MOC. I also met one of the editors of the *Journal of Medical Practice Management* as well at the Library of Congress. We discussed my experiences with the State Board of Medicine and she encouraged me to write an article about it, which was later published.[7] The Library of Congress experience was an eye-opener for me and it helped to further expand my horizons.

Since then, I have continued to be very active in both organized medicine and grassroots advocacy by writing articles, raising my voice loudly on social media, and serving on the board of trustees for my state and county medical societies. I have also done several podcasts and been interviewed on various health-care subjects.

This is quite a transformation from where I started. My lawsuits were a crucible for me, but as emotionally devastating as they were, I did evolve and grow stronger because of them. My lawyer was correct when he advised that the sun would come up thereafter. It took a lot longer than I expected, but the caterpillar eventually became a butterfly. I am stronger, more confident, and more focused because of what I have experienced. I am not the same person as I was before the lawsuits. I do not want anyone to go through what I endured, but the truth is that I have benefited because of them. My life has been incredibly enriched by my advocacy work, both in organized medicine and at a grassroots level.

I wish the divide between the two did not exist, as both groups play a pivotal role in trying to effect meaningful change. I want more physicians to support organized medicine. Most importantly, it is my fervent desire that more physicians will support our profession in general. Unfortunately, seeing patients all day is not enough. We must strive to preserve our profession and that requires speaking out against the injustices that hurt us and our patients. Much has been written about how physicians are systematically being devalued for ulterior purposes.[5,47,195] Frankly, I fear that this progressive disregard for our profession will eventually lead to its demise, with physicians serving as mere pawns on the grand corporate chessboard. If that happens, as always, it will be our patients who will be checkmated. That affects all of us because ultimately, all of us are or will become patients.

Chapter 12

Hydroxychloroquine

Advocacy does not take a vacation because a pandemic begins. If anything, advocacy efforts need to increase as new problems present themselves and old problems resurface. The year 2020 started innocently enough. I had announced my plans for retirement, and starting in January, I began to wind down. I was only working three days a week and had also stopped accepting new patients. Then Covid reared its head in March, and everyone's world turned upside down. This created all kinds of new problems separate from the obvious public health concern.

One of the initial issues was the battle for Personal Protective Equipment (PPE) for health-care workers. PPE was necessary to help limit the spread of Covid and protect those on the front lines, but it was in short supply. Often, PPE had to be reused over and over. Nurses in some cases wore garbage bags as an alternative.[196] Health-care workers were chastised or threatened by administrators for their desire for personal safety.[197] In some cases, clinicians were told not to wear masks as it might scare patients. Although social media was filled with stories such as these, many critics remained anonymous due to fear of retribution by hospital administrations. In one well-publicized case, a physician was fired for speaking out on the lack of protective equipment.[198] Even as late as December 2020, PPE was still in short supply.[199]

Existing issues such as physician documentation and scope of practice became more relevant during Covid. Regulatory requirements were relaxed at the onset of Covid with regard to quality reporting.[200] The hope was that these requirements would continue to be relaxed once the pandemic was over. With the need for more health-care workers, scope of practice restrictions were also eased. NPs argued that these restrictions should be maintained once the pandemic was over. This continues to be an area of controversy.

ABIM suspended its spring recertification exam. They subsequently extended the deadline to complete board-certification requirements, initially to the end of 2021, and then through 2022.

Covid accelerated the advent of telemedicine as we strove to limit personal contact. Physicians learned that in many cases, we could provide appropriate care virtually. Telemedicine is not perfect, as it does not allow for physical exam in most cases, but it is still a major advance in our ability to care for patients. There are strong advocacy efforts to make sure physicians are appropriately reimbursed for telemedicine.

While all of these were very important issues, my personal focus was on the issue of physician autonomy, specifically as it related to the use of the drug hydroxychloroquine (HCQ) in treating Covid and physicians' ability or inability to prescribe it.

Hydroxychloroquine is a drug that is very familiar to the rheumatology community. It is used to treat lupus, RA, and other autoimmune diseases and is generally accepted as a mild, safe, and effective drug. It has also been used to treat and prevent malaria.

I first heard about HCQ as a potential therapy for Covid early in March 2020. I picked up a prescription on March 16 to have at home in case anyone in my family became ill. I thought nothing of it at the time.

HCQ was quietly minding its own business with minimal publicity until it was suddenly thrust into the limelight on March 19 when President Trump exalted it as a potential game changer in treating Covid.[201] It quickly became a referendum on Trump with opinions on efficacy and safety based more on political leanings than the scientific data. Examples ranged from headlines in the *Washington Post* reading "From Fox News—A Big Dose of Dumb on Hydroxychloroquine"[202] to the opposing view from Tucker Carlson that "They [the press] Opposed Finding a Cure for Corona Virus Because They Feared It Might Give the President Some Political Advantage."[203] From a personal standpoint, I think that the politicization of this drug was abhorrent and reprehensible. Unfortunately, given the political polarization in the country, it was not surprising.

I first became immersed in the hydroxychloroquine controversy when I was asked to give grand rounds at a local hospital in early May 2020. I was originally scheduled to speak on the legislative and policy issues in Montgomery County that affect patient care. This was to be a follow-up to a similar lecture I had given five years earlier. When the pandemic hit, that subject material was deemed to be less topical under the circumstances. The use of HCQ had become quite controversial by that time. Given my experience as a rheumatologist with the use of HCQ, I was asked instead to present a lecture on HCQ and its use in Covid. I began to review the literature in depth.

I was appalled at what I found. Studies that supported or opposed the use of HCQ in Covid were equally lacking. The initial studies, which suggested a viable mechanism of action, proved to have significant deficits in their interpretations. Subsequent studies were equally inadequate in many ways. Either the studies were too small, the control and study populations were heterogeneous, or the conclusions reached were not supported by the data. Some papers directly contradicted previous studies.[204] Flawed analysis was the norm rather than the exception.

For example, a Veterans Administration (VA) study of 368 patients was frequently cited as a demonstration of HCQ's lack of efficacy in treating Covid.[205] Patients in the study were divided into three groups and received either HCQ alone, HCQ and azithromycin (AZ), or supportive treatment without HCQ. The authors reported a higher incidence of death and need for mechanical ventilation in the two groups receiving HCQ, suggesting that the drug provided no benefit. The study was deficient, however, as there were marked differences between the three groups in terms of their underlying health status. The patients who received HCQ, with or without azithromycin, were much more likely to have severe underlying disease than the patients who did not receive HCQ. It is unclear whether these patients did poorly because HCQ does not work or because they were so much sicker at baseline. The difference in baseline health status among the groups precludes any determination regarding the lack of efficacy of HCQ.

In contrast, a French study of 1061 patients treated with HCQ and AZ touted the benefits of the medication(s).[206] The authors reported that 4.3% of patients receiving the medications had poor clinical outcomes, with only eight deaths. This suggests a benefit for the combination of HCQ and AZ, but there were problems with this study as well. It was a retrospective analysis with no control group. The poor outcome patients were considerably sicker at baseline and had a mean age of 69, compared with a mean age of 42 in the patients who did well. It is therefore unclear if the drugs provided benefit. Was HCQ truly protective, or did the majority of patients do well because of their relative youth and good health at baseline? The older, sicker patients who received HCQ did not do well. There was no control group comparing young healthy patients receiving HCQ with young healthy patients who did not receive the drug. Thus, the conclusion regarding efficacy of HCQ had limited validity.

Neither of these studies was done well enough to offer any kind of true insight as to potential benefits of HCQ. This was true for most of the other studies I reviewed as well. However, that did not stop different news outlets and political groups from cherry-picking the data that supported their underlying political agenda and citing it as confirmatory evidence of their opinions. Those who lean toward the left used the VA study as evidence of lack of efficacy. Not surprisingly, right-leaning groups cited the latter study as demonstrating the benefits of the drug. Similar political analysis was done on studies that assessed safety. Facts and objective analysis went out the window as political arguments took center stage.

I have often made the analogy that evaluating data is similar to shooting a bow and arrow at a target. When you shoot the bow and arrow first (form an opinion) and then draw the target around wherever the arrow lands (gather information later), you hit the bull's-eye 100% of the time. Media pundits and politicians used this strategy repeatedly to demonstrate that their analyses were on target.

In the closing remarks of my lecture, I pointed out that the data on efficacy and safety of HCQ in treating Covid were inconclusive, with tremendous bias clouding the results. Data must always be interpreted through the lens of potential bias, but in this case the bias on both sides was extreme. I explained to my audience that both the efficacy and toxicity of this drug were amplified in order to serve underlying political narratives.

I followed up my grand rounds by writing an article on HCQ for the medical journal *Physician Outlook*.[207] In that article, I explained the studies that had been done, the conclusions reached, and why so many were invalid. I emphasized the message in both my lecture and my article that, "Treatment decisions should be made by physicians and their patients without interference. Public policies forbidding the use of HCQ and threatening physicians are not appropriate."

This issue of physician autonomy was especially relevant because of pressures exerted against physicians for prescribing HCQ. In Michigan, the Department of Licensing and Regulatory Affairs threatened disciplinary action against physicians who used HCQ in Covid. The agency sent a letter out on March 24 that warned physicians and pharmacists of potential professional consequences for the prescribing of hydroxychloroquine in Covid.[208] This was only five days after Trump initially promoted the use of the drug. That short time frame is indicative of how fast HCQ became a hot-button topic. The letter specifically stated:

> Prescribing hydroxychloroquine or chloroquine without further proof of efficacy for treating COVID-19 or with the intent to stockpile the drug may create a shortage for patients with lupus, rheumatoid arthritis, or other ailments for which chloroquine and hydroxychloroquine are proven treatments. Reports of this conduct will be evaluated and may be further investigated for administrative action.[209]

Governor Gretchen Whitmer received criticism from the right for the letter and the letter was subsequently rescinded. It was explained that the intent of the letter was solely to prevent hoarding of the drug for Covid patients as this would diminish the availability for patients with rheumatic conditions. The threat of administrative action was reportedly a simple miscommunication.[210] Nevertheless, the implication was clear and sent a chilling message regarding the authority of physicians to prescribe a medication off label. Similarly, the attorney general in New Jersey also restricted the use of certain medications to treat Covid.[211] This created an additional bureaucratic hoop for physicians to jump through as they now had to justify the rationale for their use of the drug.

From my standpoint, this meant that I now had to write the diagnosis on every prescription I wrote for HCQ for my arthritic patients. That was an inconvenience, but it became more problematic when it affected the ability to get the drug for one of my patients, "LP," who had Sjogren's syndrome. Sjogren's is an autoimmune disease related to lupus and is characterized primarily by dry eyes and mouth. HCQ is the primary drug used to treat it, although it is not FDA approved for Sjogren's. In fact, there are no immunosuppressive drugs that are FDA approved for Sjogren's. LP had been taking HCQ for seven years and was doing well. When she was due for her prescription, however, the insurer denied it, citing that its use in Sjogren's was off label. This insurer was usurping my right and my responsibility to prescribe a medicine off label when it was the appropriate choice for this patient. Prescription authority needs to rest with the physician, not the insurer, not the legislature, and not the media. That has been the most salient point of my advocacy as it relates to this drug.

This concept became important on a personal level when two weeks after I gave the grand rounds talk, my wife Suzan suddenly lost her sense of smell.

This was one of the possible presenting symptoms of Covid. Fortunately, she had no shortness of breath, cough, or fever. In fact, she was otherwise asymptomatic. Nonetheless, we quarantined her for two weeks. By the end of May, there was already quite a bit of public pressure on physicians not to write new prescriptions for HCQ for patients to have on hand and not for family members, but as noted, I already had acquired a prescription before the controversy had started. Now in the face of the data I had just thoroughly reviewed, I was faced with a decision whether to actually recommend it to the person I love most. As always, I weighed potential risks and benefits. Although the data regarding benefit was equivocal, I felt the safety profile was very good, based on my own 30-year experience prescribing the drug, and I therefore opted to treat her. I have no idea if the HCQ made any difference whatsoever, but she did recover uneventfully and her sense of smell ultimately returned. This was as it should be, an individual physician and his patient, in this case my wife, making a mutual decision on how to address a medical problem.

The controversy on HCQ amplified further in July, when a group of doctors from a right-wing political organization known for spreading misinformation about the pandemic,[212] promoted HCQ as an absolute cure for Covid.[213] They delivered a speech on the steps of the Supreme Court, where one speaker declared:

> This virus has a cure. It is called hydroxychloroquine, zinc, and Zithromax. I know you people want to talk about a mask. Hello? You don't need (a) mask. There is a cure. I know they don't want to open schools. No, you don't need people to be locked down. There is prevention and there is a cure.[214]

I was stunned by the misinformation they were presenting. Their video was widely panned and was subsequently taken down by social media platforms, but not before it had been viewed more than 14 million times on Facebook alone.[214] The video was also shared by President Trump and Donald Jr. in numerous ways.[215]

This video created a significant conflict in my mind regarding censorship versus the distribution of false information. Do social media companies have an obligation to allow individuals to express their opinions, even if they are deemed to be harmful to public health? Alternatively, do they have a responsibility to shut down the spread of potentially harmful misinformation? Who gets to decide what constitutes misinformation? In this case, the misinformation was fairly obvious, but what if it were not so clear cut. This issue is not limited to HCQ. As one example, there are currently similar discussions regarding Covid vaccines.

When social media platforms removed the video, there were multiple accusations regarding free speech and first amendment rights. However, this was not censorship by the government, and it therefore did not violate first amendment rights. That did not stop President Trump from filing a lawsuit against Facebook, Twitter, and YouTube.[216] Although these are private companies who are not subject to first amendment provisions, their actions raise concerns, nonetheless.

The issue of free speech versus potential harm to the community is quite contentious with valid arguments on both sides. I felt that in this case commentary was required, and that I was qualified to provide it. To that end, I wrote another article addressing the entire controversy of HCQ, especially the political aspect, along with a discussion as to whether censorship is appropriate when misinformation is being conveyed.[217]

I explained in the article how the drug had become a political football, and that the data on efficacy was equivocal at best. I did not advocate for or against its use in Covid, but once again, I strongly stated that physicians should be the ones making the decision whether or not to prescribe.

As for the censorship issue, I was ambivalent, as I feel that conflicts such as this must be decided on a case-by-case basis. I thought that this situation might have been better handled by issuing a disclaimer to the video as opposed to taking it down completely. I had concerns that removing the video would only serve to give more ammunition to those who would be inclined to believe it in the first place. I also had general concerns regarding censorship. Despite that, the statements made by this group were inappropriate, inaccurate, and dangerous.

Individual rights are a hallmark of our society, but they are not all-encompassing, and they do not automatically take precedence over societal needs. People must stop at red lights, obey the speed limit, and drive on the correct side of the road. These are part of the social contract and are public safety issues. They are not viewed as violations of individual rights. I have yet to hear anyone complain that their right to drive as fast as they want is being violated by the speed limit. The old adage is that one person's rights stop where another person's rights begin.

Should speech be any different, when one is expressing opinions that are harmful to the public at large? One could argue that this precedent would allow social media platforms to simply suppress any opinion that does not align with their underlying political agenda, but is that any different from what happens at Fox or CNN? There is a difference between speech that expresses an opposing opinion and speech that is dangerous or untruthful, or promotes violence or hatred. Private businesses are free to decide what speech and what behavior they will allow in their establishment. There have been all kinds of stories about people complaining about how mandates for masks violate their rights. Yet there are no objections to signs that read, "No shoes, No shirt, No service" as a similar violation of those rights. Maybe that is because masks are political and shoes and shirts aren't. Perhaps if we all focused a little more on our responsibilities to each other and to society as a whole, and a little less on our own "rights," we might all be better off in this world. End of diatribe. Back to HCQ.

As more studies came out, further data suggested that HCQ has a minimal, if any, role in treating Covid. It has fallen out of the mainstream discussion since Trump left the White House and has been replaced by controversies over vaccines and masks as individual rights are once again pitted against the public welfare.

The main issue with hydroxychloroquine for me was never whether or not it works in Covid. The controversy was always about who gets to decide that. Is it the treating physician, along with their patient, who should decide treatment strategies, or should regulatory agencies and insurers be able to control what a physician can and cannot prescribe? If this latter mentality is applied to a highly political scenario such as HCQ in Covid, it can potentially be extended to other drugs and other conditions, such as occurred in LP. If regulatory agencies and by extension, insurers, are allowed to make these kinds of decisions as opposed to physicians, will they do so with the patient's best interest in mind, or will financial conflicts of interests dictate the decisions made? We are already seeing this scenario play out in other arenas and I maintain that it is harmful to patients.

There is a common theme that emerges over and over again in the form of a continued distrust of physicians to take care of patients appropriately. This is expressed by insurers in terms of prior authorization, ABIM in terms of MOC, and now regulatory agencies in terms of Covid management. HCQ is just one more example of how that distrust is being propagated, in this case for political capital.

PART III

RESOLUTION

Chapter 13

Solutions?

I have laid out a number of the issues that ultimately compromise the care that patients receive. Most of these are associated with potential financial gain for a third party or control of decision-making, with progressive devaluation of physicians serving as a means toward those ultimate goals. The end result is damage to the patient-physician relationship, increased physician disenchantment, and a loss of the humanity in health care.

So what are the solutions to the health-care mess we are in? To put it bluntly, there are none. Similar to most forms of arthritis, there are no cures here. That does not mean that there are not available treatments. In many cases, symptoms can be addressed, even if the underlying diseases cannot. We cannot cure greed or eliminate the lust for power. As long as those two ambitions play a significant role in the formation of health-care policies, our health-care system will be less than optimal. Unfortunately, they are tumors that are essentially inoperable. The best we can hope to do is provide palliative care.

Fortunately, there are some measures that can be taken to help preserve the patient-physician relationship and protect the human connection that is so vital to good health care. That can only happen if we recognize the root problems and speak out against them loudly and often.

Our health-care system is a perfect storm. There are numerous barriers to making appropriate health care available to as many people as possible.

Health-care services are expensive, which makes accessing them difficult for people without reliance on third parties. This creates the potential for exploitation by those parties for financial gain. The insertion of middlemen between patients and physicians in terms of insurers, PBMs, and even the government, has clouded so many issues and compromised patient care as a result. It has removed control from the individual patient. Lowering costs to an affordable level would help to restore control to patients, where it belongs. That is easier said than done.

There are specific actions which can be taken to reduce costs. Removing the influence of middlemen as much as possible would reduce the inherent discrepancy between consumer and purchaser. I have noted that value can only be defined when the purchaser and consumer are the same entity. If an insurer is the one defining value, there is a conflict, as the physician is now obligated to the insurer as well as the patient. One model to correct this is Direct Primary Care as described in Chapter 7.[64,65] Greater acceptance of this model would help to restore the patient-physician relationship by removing the middlemen from routine encounters. Of course, doing so would not be popular with insurers as it would interfere with their business model. Another example would be to limit the role of PBMs as discussed in Chapter 8. Repeal of the safe harbor exemption would not solve all of the problems regarding the costs of medications, but it would be a healthy start. We will have to see how the HHS-OIG ruling plays out in early 2023.[94]

Educating patients and addressing social determinants of health[218,219] would also be beneficial in lowering health-care costs in general. Disparities in economics, neighborhood, education, and access to resources, including transportation and even access to food, all play a role in the health of a population in general. Improving these parameters would promote better health in the community and lower overall costs. Health care is not just about treating those who are ill. It is also about health maintenance and disease prevention.

Health care requires extensive training for those who provide it and the general public has limited knowledge of what it entails. Thus, it is ripe for misinformation. I mentioned the importance of patient education, but one of the critical barriers to that is the rampant lack of trust, in the government, in health-care experts, and in physicians themselves. Some seeds of mistrust have been deliberately planted by those with financial agendas. Some have been sown in the name of political ambition. Measures that encourage continuity of care with one physician can go a long way toward establishing trust and promoting good health habits, which would lower the costs for everyone. It is much harder to establish trust when the patient and the physician do not know each other well.

One of the reasons that lack of trust exists is because of how politically charged health care has become. I alluded to that in Chapter 12 when I referenced varying opinions regarding hydroxychloroquine. The dichotomy has been especially prevalent since Covid started, with opinions on masks and vaccines passing as surrogates for political views. Similar to HCQ, both masks and vaccines have served as a referendum on President Trump, rather than on Covid and science. The battle between individual rights and public welfare has become quite heated. Public health should not be the political issue it has become. Unfortunately, many of our leaders feel differently and have been very willing to spread misinformation in exchange for perceived political gain, regardless of how it affects the public.

In my mind, politics boils down to two simple questions. How much of an obligation do the "haves" (the young, the healthy, and the rich) owe to the "have nots" (the elderly, the sick, and the poor)? The second question is whether individual people or the government should decide the extent of their obligation. How one answers these questions is associated with where they lie on the political spectrum. Because of the increasing political polarization over the last few years, opinions regarding health care have diverged even further.

One of the basic controversies in health care is the concept of "rights." I alluded to individual rights in the last chapter, but in this case, the question is whether health care itself is a right that government owes to the public. As always, there are two sides, each with valid arguments. On the one hand, there are the logistical issues. How do we pay for health care? If health care is a right, how do we define who should provide that care and what health care should be provided? Once-a-year physical? Routine vaccinations? Sick visits? Cardiac catheterization? Expensive biologic medications for RA? Experimental treatment for a rare form of cancer? On the other hand, how can we let people suffer or die due to a lack of health care? Is it acceptable that some people have to choose between having health care and putting food on the table?

These are not easy questions. There is a wide divergence of opinions as to the optimal role of government in health care. Where should the line be drawn in terms of what health care should be provided and to whom? Do we view two patients who need hip replacements equally if one is a 60-year-old who is employed full time, and the other is a bedridden 90-year-old with dementia and numerous other health problems? Do we make a distinction based entirely on age? What if the patients above are both 60 years old? Does that make a difference? How about employment status? If we set a predetermined age limit of 75, what do we do with a 76-year-old who is fully functional, working full time, and otherwise in good health? Should that patient be denied treatment based solely on age? One-size-fits-all decisions made by third parties based on age, work status, or any other individual variable are not appropriate. Each case must be decided on its individual merits, based on all the variables, not just one. In a free market system, the patient and their physician would decide if the benefit is worth the cost. That would be optimal, but it cannot happen in our current system because the costs are prohibitively expensive.

I think that almost everyone, regardless of how they feel about universal health care, would agree that we do not want people to die or suffer because of a lack of health care. How to accomplish that and the price paid to achieve that is what remains in dispute. The entity that pays for health care is always of critical importance because whoever foots the bill is in a position to control how the care is provided. There are many people who have little trust in our government and therefore object to them having that control. Those who feel that way will therefore object to the prospect of universal health care. Many people also have little trust in their fellow human beings and feel they will milk the system. Trust is an extremely important determinant of opinions regarding health care, and it is currently in short supply. It is not something that can be easily regenerated.

One of the recurring themes in health care is the delicate balance between individual and population health. They are often in conflict. Individual rights to health care do not exist in a vacuum. One person's right becomes someone else's responsibility. What affects one person often affects many as we strive for some semblance of fairness and equality. These can be very difficult concepts to apply to a heterogeneous population.

I often compare health care to an all-you-can-eat buffet with a limited supply of food. If the people at the front of the line have all they can eat, there is not enough food left over to feed the people at the back of the line. If we ration the food such that there is food left over for the people at the back of the line, it no longer is "all you can eat." In that scenario, the people at the front of the line are unhappy. Either way, someone's needs or desires will not be met. If a survey were conducted as to how the restaurant should distribute food, the people at the front of the line and the people at the back of the line would have vastly different answers.

The Affordable Care Act served to invite more people into the restaurant but did not increase the food supply. Some of these people will get food they otherwise would not have received, but others will get less food as a result. The only way to solve this problem is to bring in more food. That is why some have pushed to increase the food supply by allowing nurse practitioners to practice medicine. The problem is that not all of the "food" in that circumstance has been adequately tested for safety or nutritional value. That is not a knock on the ability or intelligence of NPs. It is simply a commentary on the difference in quantity and content of training between NPs and physicians. One potential strategy would be to increase federal funding for residency slots to increase the number of physicians.

Health care cannot be an all-you-can-eat buffet for everyone. We simply do not have the resources, and promoting it as such is therefore detrimental. How we distribute the limited resources becomes an issue of paramount importance. Health care is not a uniform entity. Different people have different needs and different resources available to them, and everyone understandably wants and furthermore expects our health-care system to meet all of their needs. That is just not possible.

Currently, there is a sense of entitlement in our society that has led to unreasonable expectations of health care. Take a look at advertisements from insurers, pharmaceutical companies, attorneys, hospitals, and doctors that promote their services. The public has been led to believe that all medical problems should have quick, easy solutions with no risks, no side effects, and at no cost. If the problem is not solved, attorneys will then advise that it must be because someone made a mistake, such that compensation is owed.

These are not realistic scenarios. Presenting health care in that light is harmful. Expectations have been created that reality cannot meet, resulting in patient dissatisfaction. Those expectations need to be adjusted. The way to do this is through education. However, as noted previously, education will be difficult as long as there are so many mixed messages being promoted and as long as trust is lacking. We are therefore in a very difficult bind when it comes to effecting meaningful change in health care.

Having said all of this, what can be done?

Despite the limitations, patient education remains the most important factor in improving the system. This is not so easy to do given the political divide, lack of trust, and general logistics. It needs to start in school, well before adulthood. In addition to the usual health topics, such as basic anatomy, nutrition, and first aid, it would be beneficial if students were also taught about how our health-care system works, including how insurance policies work. The curriculum could also include other basic health-care issues, such as how to find and evaluate a doctor and how to get the most out of a doctor visit as well as a myriad of other issues regarding health and adult life skills in general. Students must be taught that good health does not just happen.

Transparency must also be a cornerstone of any health-care reform, both in terms of cost and in terms of who is providing care. DNPs must explain to patients that they are not medical or osteopathic doctors. Insurers must make their policies understandable to the layperson. Hospitals and pharmaceutical companies must disclose their prices.

There has been some progress in this area, but not enough. Legislation has been proposed and in some cases passed to address these issues, but compliance has been a problem. As an example, the Centers for Medicare and Medicaid Services issued the Hospital Price Transparency Rule,[220,221] which took effect on January 1, 2021. This ruling requires each hospital operating in the United States to provide clear accessible pricing information online about the items and services they provide without any barriers. The goal was to make it easier for patients to shop and compare prices before going to the hospital for a test or procedure. The hospital industry proceeded to file a lawsuit so as to not reveal their prices, but a bipartisan array of district and appeals court judges rejected every one of those legal challenges in favor of the price transparency rule.[222–224] According to a recent report from a patient rights advocacy group[225] looking at how well hospitals were adhering to this ruling, more than 94% of the 500 hospitals studied were found to be noncompliant with the mandate.[222]

Transparency is also hard to come by in the pharmaceutical industry. The Department of Health and Human Services issued a ruling in 2019 that required pharmaceutical companies to disclose costs in their direct-to-consumer ads for drugs whose list price is equal to or greater than $35 for either a month's supply or the usual course of therapy.[226] Not surprisingly, the pharmaceutical industry filed a lawsuit against HHS to prevent this. As a result, a federal appeals court issued a ruling that HHS lacks the legal authority to force drug companies to disclose prices in their TV ads.[227]

As a result, pharmaceutical companies continue to fail to address costs in a straightforward fashion. As an example, in a recent television ad for Humira,[228] the manufacturer "discloses" costs by noting that "The majority of Humira patients pay less than $5 per month. Questions about your cost? Visit Humira.com/cost." These words are not spoken. They are flashed on the screen in small print for three seconds near the end of the ad. The ad does verbally state that "if you can't afford your medicine, AbbVie may be able to help."

When we visit the Humira website, we learn that patients *could* pay $5 per month with the HUMIRA Complete Savings Card.[229] There is an asterisk in that sentence after the words "$5 per month." In the small print under the asterisk, it is noted that terms and conditions apply, and that patients must meet eligibility requirements. The co-pay assistance is not available to patients receiving prescription benefits through any government-funded program, such as Medicare Part D. Patients are not eligible if the program is prohibited by the patient's insurer. Patients residing in certain states may not be eligible (these states are not listed). The offer is subject to change or discontinuance without notice. Restrictions, including monthly maximums, may apply. For certain patients the maximal program benefit is $6,000 per year. Keeping in mind that the retail cost of Humira is $9,233, and the lowest GoodRx price for the most common version of Humira is $5,809.17,[57] that $6,000 limit for those patients only covers one month of the drug.

Transparency with regard to who is providing health-care services is not limited to discussions regarding nurse practitioners and physician assistants. It is also a problem with regard to surprise billing and in-network versus out-of-network providers.

Surprise billing occurs when a patient seeks in-network care, but unbeknownst to them, has care provided by an out-of-network provider. An example would be a patient who has surgery done at an in-network facility using an in-network surgeon, only to learn that the anesthesiologist is out of network, resulting in a separate bill that was not anticipated. In many cases, such as an emergency room visit, the patient does not even have the luxury to choose who will provide their care. Patients often do not become aware of these bills until long after the service has been rendered.

This has been an active area for advocacy efforts with some success. Recently, legislation was passed[230, 231] that will serve to protect consumers from the cost of unanticipated out-of-network medical bills. The legislation will take effect in January 2022.

Facility fees are another example of lack of transparency. A facility fee is a charge that a patient may have to pay when they see a doctor at a clinic that is not owned by that doctor. Facility fees are charged in addition to any other charges for the visit.[232] These fees typically occur at hospital-run facilities. This is why a service performed at a hospital facility may be significantly more expensive than the same service performed at an independent facility.[233] Most patients are unaware of them.

In one specific case, a patient was asked if he wanted his arthroscopic surgery to be done on a Wednesday or a Friday.[234] The difference was not simply a difference in dates. It was also a difference in locations, as the Wednesday procedure would be done at the hospital, while the Friday procedure would be done in the outpatient surgery center across the street from the hospital. The difference in cost between the two days was approximately $11,000 due to the facility fees at the hospital. If the patient had a 50% coinsurance policy, they would have had to pay more than $5,000 extra if they chose Wednesday over Friday. How many patients know to ask about this potential added expense?

These fees are permitted based on the argument that hospitals provide 24/7 care and need help with the associated overhead costs. The Centers for Medicare and Medicaid Services have attempted to curtail facility fees by introducing a site-neutral payment policy. The American Hospital Association sued over the move and plans to take the case to the Supreme Court.[235]

It is interesting to note that both hospitals and pharmaceutical companies have resorted to legal action to prevent transparency. This has applied to disclosure of hospital costs, facility fees, and disclosure of pharmaceutical costs. These serve to keep patients and physicians in the dark and maintain control for these corporate entities.

Transparency is more than just a matter of reducing costs. It is also about patient care. Hospitals typically insist that their employed physicians refer to in-network physicians, and lab and radiology facilities within their system, to prevent "leakage." This does more than just increase the facility fees every step along the way.[233] It also compromises care, as physicians are pressured to refer to another doctor within the system as opposed to the doctor they may think is best for the patient. I actually experienced this in my practice. We are an independent practice, yet the local hospital where we had privileges "encouraged" us to refer within their system. Fortunately they had no leverage over us, although that is not true for physicians whose practice is owned by the hospital. As independent physicians, we were under no obligation to comply, and we did not succumb to their requests. Nonetheless, it is an example of what goes on behind the scenes that can potentially affect the care that patients receive, not to mention the costs they accumulate.

Transparency is critical if we hope to have effective reform. In a free market system with transparency in costs and the network status of physicians and services, patients will decide who provides value with their wallets. The competition for customers will serve to lower prices. Physicians would strive to demonstrate that they are providing value to attract and keep patients, rather than engaging in the meaningless clicking of boxes to satisfy "value" requirements defined by a third party. Just as patients decide where to buy their groceries or their car, they would decide where to go for their medical care. This might even apply to using NPs as primary caregivers as long as patients know in advance who is treating them and their level of education. Transparency and education are absolutely critical building blocks if we hope to improve health care.

Another issue to be cognizant of is tort reform. While this problem is no longer front and center, it remains a concern. The introduction of certificates of merit was a great advance in 2002, but they must be used with integrity. Some physicians who provide written statements for a fee are nothing more than shameless mercenaries, willing to offer any testimony in exchange for a fee. I experienced that personally. I recognize the need for a witness to be protected from unscrupulous threats which otherwise may make them reluctant to provide honest testimony. However, complete immunity as occurred in my case, gives the witness license to say whatever they want without any potential repercussions, no matter how egregious their testimony is. There must be some opportunity for recourse against those who make blatantly false statements in a certificate of merit or in expert testimony. That recourse was not available to me and I suffered as a result.

One potential solution regarding certificates of merit would be to prescreen potential legal cases through a central independent organization, such as the state licensure board. In this model, physicians would be required to review one case yearly, if needed, as a prerequisite for licensure renewal. That would pose a problem as physicians are already extremely busy, but analysis by an independent physician would be better than that from hired guns employed by law firms to do their bidding. Again, this may not happen frequently, but it did happen to me and almost cost me my career.

Venue remains an ongoing issue. The rules put in place in the early 2000s in Pennsylvania have served us well by redirecting lawsuits from plaintiff-friendly locales to the county where the alleged malpractice took place. Patients must have appropriate redress if they have been wronged, but there must be balance between the patient's ability to recover damages when they have been harmed by negligence and the damage done to physicians via inappropriate lawsuits. A bad outcome does not automatically equate to malpractice having been committed. If undue pressure is exerted against physicians in the legal arena, such as would occur with reversal of the venue rules in Pennsylvania, I fear we may revert back to the malpractice crisis we experienced 20 years ago. It is imperative that the venue rulings from the early 2000s are not overturned.

Next comes the issue of regulatory oversight. I have emphasized that everything in medicine is about finding the balance between risks and benefits. This applies to regulatory oversight as well, and everyone, myself included, has their own biases as to how regulations should be implemented.

Regulations need to be increased in some areas and decreased in others. On the one hand, there needs to be increased regulatory oversight with regard to PBMs and insurance policies such as prior authorization, peer to peers, and kickbacks, which serve to compromise individual patient care in the name of profit. However, regulatory agencies should not overstep their bounds by dictating which medications physicians may or may not prescribe. Physicians already are regulated in terms of licensing and continuing medical education requirements. Furthermore, the legal system always serves as potential oversight. Physicians who do not practice good medicine are subject to penalties in the legal arena.

The preeminent concept to always think about with regard to regulatory oversight is how a particular regulation will affect patient care. We must consider why regulations exist and who they serve. Do MACRA and excessive documentation requirements actually serve to benefit patients? I think not. Physicians, rather than legislators or insurers, are in the best position to determine how best to care for patients. The problem is that insurers, corporations, and bureaucrats are not necessarily incentivized to allow physician input. The result is a mountain of bureaucracy designed to limit the role of physicians in patient care.

Randall Cunningham, former quarterback of the Philadelphia Eagles, once said "Let me be me,"[236] when he was being harangued and critiqued by reporters as to what he should be doing. I feel the same way about health care. Let physicians be physicians. Let us do what we were trained to do.

I firmly believe that if we create policies whose focus is on what is best for patients, the rest will take care of itself. Physicians are the ones most equipped to understand the potential unexpected ramifications of new health-care policies. Regulatory agencies and the legislature must be nimble enough to amend polices when unintended consequences occur that are detrimental to patient care.

We need to have greater involvement of the physician community in decision-making, specifically physicians who take care of patients every day as opposed to those who work administratively or in academia. Yes, there are economic variables that require expertise beyond what physicians can offer, but the best assessment for optimizing patient care comes from those who do it every day. Of course, physicians must be willing to take on this responsibility. Currently, very few are willing to do so.

Changes to improve health-care policy are not just incumbent on organizations such as the AMA or the legislature. Change also has to happen one physician, one patient at a time. Physicians must take the lead here, but I fear that apathy and burnout have set in and poisoned the chance to effect significant change. I have not been nearly as successful as I would have liked in getting physicians involved in protecting our profession and more importantly, our patients.

To that end, there needs to be greater education of physicians with instruction regarding business models and the politics of health care included in medical school curriculums. Physicians are generally not good advocates, in part because we were never taught how to do it. Often it takes a striking event, such as a lawsuit in my case, to wake people up.

There are no easy solutions to the problems we face in health care. We are too polarized with no consensus on what is optimal. In many cases, there are no viable solutions at all unless certain prerequisites such as education, transparency, and financial incentives for third parties are addressed. Perhaps the most important thing is combating the apathy that exists in the medical profession.[51] If physicians are not willing to fight for our profession and for our patients, who will?

What does the future hold for health care? I do not have a crystal ball. I have no expertise in economics, health-care policy, or public health. I can only go by what I have seen and what I have learned. I believe that we are headed toward a socialized system of health care as exists in most other countries. The Affordable Care Act and the corporatization of health care are steps in that direction. I think that this will benefit some, to the detriment of others.

Dividing a pizza into more slices means that more people will get to eat. However, the size of each slice will be smaller. I can invite three friends over to share one pizza and each of us will get two slices. I can invite seven friends over and each of us will get one slice. I can invite 15 friends over and each of us will get half a slice. Socialized medicine will not allow me to invite 15 friends over and have everyone get two slices. The only way that happens is if we increase the number of physicians, which would be analogous to ordering more pizza. The alternative is to bring in another food by allowing those without medical expertise to practice medicine.

Along those lines, I do believe that scope of practice creep will continue. The value of a medical education will be minimized even further as those without one will be allowed to practice medicine. Ultimately, that may well lead to a two-tier system. Those who can afford to do so will see physicians, while government-supplied health care will more often use nurse practitioners and physician assistants. The number of physicians will decrease even further, as there will be reduced incentive to go to medical school, just as was described by the physician assistant in Chapter 10.

Mass production assembly-line health care will replace individual expertise in health care as it has in other endeavors in our society. The humanity in health care will be squeezed out even further as providers follow preordained algorithms without the flexibility to adapt to individual circumstances. None of this bodes well for health care, but the public will slowly adapt to these constraints. Convenience will replace the patient-physician relationship in terms of importance. We are already seeing this dynamic happening.

I also think that artificial intelligence will play a more prominent role in terms of defining diagnosis and treatment. That definitely has advantages if used properly, but if used exclusively, the price we will pay is the loss of human instincts and qualities, such as empathy and compassion. A hand on a shoulder for a patient in distress can go a long way as can validation for the suffering that patients experience. Sometimes simply listening to a patient without saying a word can be very powerful. Can artificial intelligence do that? I question if artificial intelligence would have recognized that something was not right with my patient, AS, with the subdural hematoma, described in Chapter 5. That diagnosis was made only because I knew her so well. There is more to medicine than just making diagnoses and prescribing treatments. The human connection is something we are sacrificing in the process. It is not something we should give up without a fight.

The only way this changes is if enough people understand these issues and are willing to speak out against them. We must be able to set aside our political differences to have any shot at this. Admittedly, that is not likely to happen, given the current environment.

The load cannot be carried by a few leaders. Mostly we have to decide as a society what we want: individualized health care, or cookie-cutter, one-size-fits-all, corporate health care. We are not at a fork in the road. We are at a fork in the river. If we do not consciously make a decision to paddle in one direction, the current will take us the other way.

That is why advocacy is so important. We cannot solve all of the problems, but there are some that can be addressed that serve most people, most of the time, such as transparency and public education. These are issues that most people can agree upon, regardless of political persuasion. The only people who do not benefit from the proposed reforms are the bureaucrats and the middlemen.

A quote that has been attributed to both Wayne Gretzky and Michael Jordan says, "You miss 100% of the shots you do not take." Too many physicians choose to not even try. I may strike out in my endeavors, but at least when I go to my deathbed, I will have pride in knowing that I was willing to step into the batter's box and take my swings. I can now look my daughters in the eye and tell them that I did indeed fight for what was right. That was something I had questioned in myself after I agreed to settle the lawsuit. Learning to do that has been so valuable to me. However, that is not the most important lesson I have learned throughout all of this.

Chapter 14

Retirement

In 2019, I made the decision official by announcing that I would retire at the end of 2020, after 31 years in practice with more than 100,000 patient visits. Covid played no role in my decision. It did not exist at the time of my decision, and there was no way to know how 2020 would ultimately play out. I decided to make my retirement effective on December 31, 2020, which was the last day before my board certification would run out. I wanted to maintain my practice for as long as possible, and I knew that once I relinquished my certification, I would not be able to continue to practice. Ironically, in view of Covid, ABIM initially extended my board certification to the end of 2021 and now even further to the end of 2022. Thus, I will remain board certified for an extra two years beyond what I anticipated, provided I pay the fees. I have not done so and do not plan to do so. ABIM has not yet changed my certification status, but they will as soon as they realize I am not going to give them any more money. At that point, my board certification will be revoked and I will no longer be considered "qualified to practice" rheumatology. I refuse to subsidize ABIM's efforts and I continue to speak out against them, even after retirement.

Announcing my retirement caused me to become introspective. Even now, having been retired for almost a year, I regularly think back to all that I experienced in my career, both good and bad. I realize now that my legal situations, as traumatic as they were, actually changed my life for the better. They spurred me on to speak out against injustices in health care. I reflect on the many colleagues I have met from across the country and the friendships I have made as a result. I think about the advocacy work that we continue to pursue. The bottom line is that I have been incredibly lucky with a career that I could never have imagined when I started out. How could I possibly have envisioned having my picture in

Time and *USA Today*, writing articles in medical journals or being interviewed by the *New York Times*, along with trips to Washington and Harrisburg to speak with legislators? Somehow along the way, I even learned about the differences between Democrats and Republicans. I had no true writing experience previously, so there was no way to anticipate that I would write numerous articles and op-eds, much less a book. Being asked to do national podcasts and getting the opportunity to speak at the Library of Congress are incomprehensible to me even now. I feel extremely blessed as I reminisce.

As 2020 progressed, I said my goodbyes to patients. We shed tears together. There were hugs, despite our concerns regarding Covid. The human emotions simply outweighed the fears. In many cases, I said farewell via telehealth. It was nowhere near as satisfying as saying goodbye in person. I received numerous cards and letters from patients, wishing me well. They expressed sorrow that I was leaving and gratitude for the care I had provided.

As I reflect on my career, one patient in particular comes to mind. He had Churg-Strauss, a potentially life-threatening form of vasculitis (inflammation of blood vessels). When I met him, he was severely ill in the intensive care unit. I was able to shepherd him through difficult times, despite various setbacks, including a stroke that fortunately left him with only a mild limp. He survived and was discharged from the hospital. He often would come to his office visits with his wife, and we became friendly. He worked out at the same gym as I did, and I would talk with him there. One day, he informed me that he would soon be moving to Florida. His wife came in with him to his last appointment and said words that still bring tears to my eyes, even as I write this, years later. She advised me that the next time I become upset with any of the many things in health care that agitate and frustrate me, I should remember her husband. She pointed out that not only did I make a difference in her husband's life, but I also impacted the lives of all who love him and still have him around. In the years that followed, I thought of her words often, and they helped me to keep my priorities straight when bureaucracy and injustices in health care seemed insurmountable.

The single greatest joy in medicine is knowing that you have made a positive difference in someone's life. When you think about it, that is all we can really ask for as physicians. I have been fortunate to have experienced that many times. As I wrote in Chapter 1, Samuel Shem, in his novel, *The House of God*, writes that the most loving thing we can do as physicians is to "be with" the patient. We cannot always cure. We cannot always relieve suffering, but we can always "be with" the patient, that is, share their lives, commiserate in their sorrows, revel in their joys, and most importantly, validate their experiences. The caring may actually be more important than the curing. This is the "art" of medicine and is why the patient-physician relationship is the core of health care. There is no substitute.

Now that I have retired, I have mixed emotions. I do not miss the bureaucracy or the endless entry of meaningless data. I do not miss peer to peers or letters of medical necessity. I do not miss getting up early enough in the morning to start office hours at 7:00 a.m. I do not miss the feelings of being rushed when I do not have time. I do not miss getting requests for medical records and the associated anxiety as I wondered if I was about to be named in a lawsuit. I do not miss having to give patients bad news. I do not miss patients with unreasonable expectations whom I could never satisfy, regardless of what I did. Fortunately, they were in the minority. I do not miss seeing the pain and suffering that patients endure. I do not miss filling out forms that ask me when a patient will be able to return to work or how often they will need to miss work in the future. I do not miss giving a patient a prescription for six months of a medicine and then getting a refill request from the pharmacy after one month. I do not miss the self-doubts when I wondered if the decision I had made was the right one.

However, I most definitely miss the feeling of elation when a patient with active arthritis responds to treatment. I miss patients sharing their lives with me, telling me about a new grandchild, a new job, or a recent vacation. I miss the camaraderie of colleagues. I miss the intellectual stimulation of trying to solve a difficult case. I miss the joy of reading in depth about a particular patient's illness, so that I can better take care of them. I miss the learning that goes along with patient care. Reading about a disease without the context of a specific patient is not as satisfying. I miss the interactions with patients, staff, and colleagues. Mostly I miss the feeling of being able to help another human being, which was my motivation for going into medicine in the first place. Advocacy helps to fill that void.

I recognize the importance of what I have done over the years, both in advocacy and in taking care of patients. I recognize what physicians and other health-care workers across the world do every day. I applaud them for the sacrifices they make in terms of patient care. This may manifest in leaving a family event to deliver a baby, vacating one's bed at midnight to tend to a sick patient in the hospital, taking a patient's phone call while on vacation, spending a weekend researching how to provide better care for a patient, or risking exposure in the setting of a pandemic. I have never delivered a baby, but I personally have done all of those other things. They come with the territory. These sacrifices have never been more obvious than in the recent Covid crisis, especially by those on the front lines in ERs and ICUs and should never be taken for granted.

Yes, I am proud of what I have accomplished and the care I have provided, but my gratitude greatly surpasses my pride. The memories I have accumulated are a treasure whose value is priceless and one for which I will be eternally appreciative. I realize that although I have tried to benefit patients over the years, it is I who have benefited even more because my patients allowed me to "be with" them and become part of their lives. Health care is ultimately a human experience. Throughout all of this, that is the most valuable lesson I have learned. That is something worth fighting for. That is why I am a health-care advocate.

Abbreviations

AANP—American Association of Nurse Practitioners

AAPA—American Academy of Physician Assistants

ABIM—American Board of Internal Medicine

ABMS—American Board of Medical Specialties

AIDS—Acquired Immunodeficiency Syndrome

AISNHL—Autoimmune Sensorineural Hearing Loss

AMA—American Medical Association

AMAC—Association of Mature American Citizens

AVN—Avascular Necrosis

AZ—Azithromycin

CMS—Centers for Medicare and Medicaid Services

CPT—Common Procedural Terminology

DNP—Doctor of Nursing Practice

DPC—Direct Primary Care

EHR—Electronic Health Record

EPA—Enteropathic Arthritis

FDA—Food and Drug Administration

FTC—Federal Trade Commission

GAO—Government Accountability Office

GPO—Group Purchasing Organization

HCQ—Hydroxychloroquine

HHS—Health and Human Services

HHS-OIG—Health and Human Services Office of the Inspector General

IBC—Independence Blue Cross

ICD-10—International Classification of Diseases—10th version

MACRA—Medicare Access and CHIP Reauthorization Act.

MCARE—Medical Care Availability and Reduction of Error

MCMS—Montgomery County Medical Society

MIPS—Merit-based Incentive Payment System

MMSS—Medical Malpractice Stress Syndrome

MOC—Maintenance of Certification

NBPAS—National Board of Physicians and Surgeons

NP—Nurse Practitioner

NSAID—Nonsteroidal Anti-Inflammatory Drug

Ob-gyn—Obstetrics and Gynecology

PA—Physician Assistant

PADS—Physicians Against Drug Shortages

PAMED—Pennsylvania Medical Society

PAPA—Politically Active Physicians Association

PBM—Pharmacy Benefit Manager

PTSD—Post-Traumatic Stress Disorder

PPE—Personal Protective Equipment

PPP—Physicians for Patient Protection

PWT—Physicians Working Together

PT—Physical Therapy

RA—Rheumatoid Arthritis

SGR—Sustainable Growth Rate

SNRA—Seronegative Rheumatoid Arthritis

VA—Veterans Administration

References

1. Sinsky, Christine MD, et al., "Allocation of Physician Time in Ambulatory Practice: A Time and Motion Study in 4 Specialties," *Annals of Internal Medicine*, December 6, 2016, Volume 165, (11) 753–760. https://www.acpjournals.org/doi/full/10.7326/M16-0961

2. Arndt, BG, "Tethered to the EHR: Primary Care Physician Workload Assessment Using EHR Event Log Data and Time-Motion Observations," *Annals of Family Medicine*, Sept–Oct 2017, Volume 15, (5), 419–426. https://www.annfammed.org/content/15/5/419

3. Gabler, Ellen, "How Chaos at Chain Pharmacies is Putting Patients at Risk," *New York Times*, Jan 31, 2020. https://www.nytimes.com/2020/01/31/health/pharmacists-medication-errors.html?searchResultPosition=1

4. Mandel, Melissa, "The Women's Medical College of Pennsylvania," *The Encyclopedia of Greater Philadelphia*. https://philadelphiaencyclopedia.org/archive/womans-medical-college-of-pennsylvania/#:~:text=It%20was%20the%20longest%2Dlasting,the%20Medical%20College%20of%20Pennsylvania

5. Lopatin M, MD, "The Devaluation of Physicians," Kevin MD, Jun 19, 2019. https://www.kevinmd.com/blog/2019/06/the-devaluation-of-physicians.html

6. It should be noted throughout this book that initials or first names are used instead of actual full names of patients. In all cases, the initials or first name used are not the patient's actual initials or name.

7. Lopatin M, MD, "The Facts Did Not Matter: One Physician's Experience with the State Board of Medicine," *Journal of Medical Practice Management*, Volume 33, Number 2, Sept/Oct 2017, 108–110.

8. Tayoun, J, "Dying for Help: Are Patients Needlessly Suffering Due to the High Cost of Medical Liability Insurance," Oct 1, 2003. https://books.google.com/books?id=NpBjvitcVrkC&pg=PA133&lpg=PA133&dq=P.A.P.A.+politically+

active+physicians+association&source=bl&ots=PlfZOhY1SS&sig=ACfU3U0SK-fWaQRDAeSZ-7TVVPO-q58f-NQ&hl=en&sa=X&ved=2ahUKEwjrv_XE0IL-wAhWQXM0KHaQqDCUQ6AEwA3oECAYQAw#v=onepage&q=P.A.P.A.%20politically%20active%20physicians%20association&f=false

9. Lopatin M, MD, "I Knew She Was Trouble," *Medical Economics*, June 4, 2004, 39–41. https://judiciary.pasenategop.com/wp-content/uploads/sites/42/2020/09/Article-Mark-Lopatin-MD.pdf

10. Jena AB, MD, et al., "Malpractice Risk According to Physician Specialty," *New England Journal of Medicine*, Aug 18, 2011, 365:629–636. https://www.nejm.org/doi/full/10.1056/NEJMsa1012370

11. Balch CM, "Personal Consequences of Malpractice Lawsuits on American Surgeons," J American College of Surgeons, Nov 2011,213 (5) 657–667. https://pubmed.ncbi.nlm.nih.gov/21890381/

12. Scibilia J, MD, FAAP, "Medical malpractice stress syndrome can affect physical, mental health," AAP News, 2020. https://www.aappublications.org/news/2020/08/01/wellness080120

13. Gómez-Durán EL, et al., "Physicians as second victims after a malpractice claim: An important issue in need of attention," *Journal of Healthcare Quality Research*, Sept–Oct 2018, Vol. 33. Issue 5. 284–289. https://www.elsevier.es/en-revista-journal-healthcare-quality-research-257-articulo-physicians-as-second-victims-after-S2603647918300526

14. Charles S, MD, et al., "Physicians' Self-Reports of Reactions to Malpractice Litigation," *American Journal of Psychiatry*, Apr 1984, 141 (4) 563–565. https://pubmed.ncbi.nlm.nih.gov/6703136/

15. Studdert DM, et al., "Defensive Medicine Among High-Risk Specialist Physicians in a Volatile Malpractice Environment," *JAMA*, Jun 1, 2005, 293 (21) 2609–2617. https://jamanetwork.com/journals/jama/fullarticle/200994

16. "Fear of Litigation Study," conducted by Harris Interactive, Final Report, April 11, 2002. https://aspe.hhs.gov/basic-report/addressing-new-health-care-crisis-reforming-medical-litigation-system-improve-quality-health-care#note45

17. Mello MM, et al., "National costs of the Medical Liability System," *Health Affairs*. 2010 Sep;29(9):1569–1577. https://www.ncbi.nlm.nih.gov/pmc/articles/PMC3048809/

18. PricewaterhouseCoopers. "The factors fueling rising healthcare costs 2006." https://www.pwc.com/il/he/publications/assets/4the_factors_fueling.pdf

19. https://www.cms.gov/Research-Statistics-Data-and-Systems/Statistics-Trends-and-Reports/NationalHealthExpendData/NationalHealthAccounts Historical

20. https://truecostofhealthcare.org/wp-content/uploads/2015/02/defensivemedicine_ebook_final.pdf

21. Letourneau, R, "Defensive Medicine Adds Billions to Annual U.S. Healthcare Costs," *Health Care Finance*, Sep 21, 2011. https://www.healthcarefinancenews.com/news/defensive-medicine-adds-650b-850b-annual-healthcare-costs

22. Statement of The Honorable James Greenwood, The Patient Access Crisis – The Role of Medical Litigation: Joint Hearing Before the Committee on the Judiciary and the Committee on Health, Education, Labor and Pensions, Feb 11, 2003, P 139. https://books.google.com/books?id=NiZXrykad08C&pg=PA139&lpg=PA139&dq=Statement+of+The+Honorable+James+Greenwood,+The+Patient+Access+Crisis-+The+Role+of+Medical+Litigation.+Joint+Hearing+Before+the+Committee+on+the+Judiciary+and+the+Committee+on+Health,+Education,&source=bl&ots=-JGqaSDt7E&sig=ACfU3U1X38GejLwl-275J4g3Vvvo6nKQ-3g&hl=en&sa=X&ved=2ahUKEwij-7K6m6fyAhXKVN8K-HeO_DEQQ6AF6BAgCEAM#v=onepage&q=Statement%20of%20The%20Honorable%20James%20Greenwood%2C%20The%20Patient%20Access%20Crisis-%20The%20Role%20of%20Medical%20Litigation.%20Joint%20Hearing%20Before%20the%20Committee%20on%20the%20Judiciary%20and%20the%20Committee%20on%20Health%2C%20Education%2C&f=false

23. "P.A.P.A. To Lead Malpractice Protest Starting April 28th," *Insurance Journal*, Apr 22, 2003. https://www.insurancejournal.com/news/east/2003/04/22/28191.htm

24. Malfitano, N, "Philadelphia Remains the No. 1 'Judicial Hellhole,' Now Joined by Pa. Supreme Court," *Pennsylvania Record*, Dec 8, 2020. https://pennrecord.com/stories/568281908-philadelphia-remains-the-no-1-judicial-hellhole-now-joined-by-pa-supreme-court

25. "Addressing the New Health Care Crisis: Reforming the Medical Litigation System to Improve the Quality of Health Care," Office of the Assistant Secretary for Planning and Evaluation, Mar 2, 2003. https://aspe.hhs.gov/basic-report/addressing-new-health-care-crisis-reforming-medical-litigation-system-improve-quality-health-care

26. Kessler, D, McClellan, M, "Do Doctors Practice Defensive Medicine?" *The Quarterly Journal of Economics*, May, 1996, Vol. 111, No. 2, 353–390. https://liabilityinnovation.files.wordpress.com/2015/11/kessler-mcclellan-1996.pdf

27. https://en.wikipedia.org/wiki/Most-wanted_Iraqi_playing_cards

28. Levy S, Kane L, Medscape Malpractice Report 2017, Nov 15, 2017. https://www.medscape.com/slideshow/2017-malpractice-report-6009206?src=wnl_physrep_171114_mscpmrk_malpractice2017&uac=129504DJ&impID=1482884&faf=1

29. Studdert, DM et al., "Claims, Errors and Compensation Payments in Medical Malpractice Litigation," *New England Journal of Medicine*, May 1, 2006, 354: 2024–2033.

30. Localio, AR, JD et al., "Relation Between Malpractice Claims and Adverse Events Due to Negligence – Results of the Harvard Medical Practice III," *New England Journal of Medicine*, Jul 25, 1991, 325: 245–251. https://www.nejm.org/doi/full/10.1056/nejm199107253250405

31. https://www.legis.state.pa.us/cfdocs/legis/li/uconsCheck.cfm?yr=2002&sessInd=0&act=13

32. Kersh, R "The Politics of Medical Malpractice in Pennsylvania, 1975–2005," The Project on Medical Liability in Pennsylvania, funded by Pew Charitable Trusts, 25. https://www.pewtrusts.org/-/media/legacy/uploadedfiles/wwwpewtrustsorg/reports/medical_liability/politicsofmedmalinpakersh0206pdf.pdf

33. http://www.pacodeandbulletin.gov/Display/pacode?file=/secure/pacode/data/231/chapter1000/s1042.3.html&searchunitkeywords=certificate%2Cof%2Cmerit&origQuery=certificate%20of%20merit&operator=OR&title=nullhttp://www.pacodeandbulletin.gov/Display/pacode?file=/secure/pacode/data/231/chapter1000/s1042.3.html&searchunitkeywords=certificate%2Cof%2Cmerit&origQuery=certificate%20of%20merit&operator=OR&title=null

34. Kersh, R, "The Politics of Medical Malpractice in Pennsylvania, 1975–2005," The Project on Medical Liability in Pennsylvania, funded by Pew Charitable Trusts, 28–29. https://www.pewtrusts.org/-/media/legacy/uploadedfiles/www-pewtrustsorg/reports/medical_liability/politicsofmedmalinpakersh0206pdf.pdf

35. "Governor Corbett Signs 'Fair Share Act,' Important Tort Reforms Now Law," Cision, Jun 28, 2011. https://www.prnewswire.com/news-releases/governor-corbett-signs-fair-share-act-important-tort-reforms-now-law-124663103.html

36. Mitchell, Max, "PA Superior Court Ruling Opens Door for Plaintiffs to Avoid Fair Share Act Application, Attorneys Say," March 24, 2021, *The Legal Intelligencer*. https://www.law.com/thelegalintelligencer/2021/03/24/pa-superior-court-ruling-opens-door-for-plaintiffs-to-avoid-fair-share-act-application-attorneys-say/?slreturn=20210410120927#:~:text=Where%20there%20is%20no%20liability,Johnson

37. "Proposed Venue Rule Change for Medical Professional Liability Actions in Pennsylvania," Pennsylvania Medical Society, Mar 2019. https://www.pamedsoc.org/docs/librariesprovider2/pamed-documents/venue-change-medical-liability_overview.pdf?sfvrsn=509f1b93_4

38. Unified Judicial System of Pennsylvania. http://www.pacourts.us/news-and-statistics/research-and-statistics/medical-malpractice-statistics

39. Lopatin, M, MD, "Are Physicians Allowed To Be Human?", *Journal of Medicine*, Feb 1, 2020. https://www.ncnp.org/journal-of-medicine/2492-are-physicians-allowed-to-be-human.html

40. Himmelstein, D, MD, Personal communication 11/22/21

41. Njolomole, M, "Thomas Sowell on the Welfare State," The American Experiment, Mar 5, 2020. https://www.americanexperiment.org/thomas-sowell-on-the-welfare-state/

42. Kane, Leslie, MA, "Medscape National Physician Burnout and Suicide Report 2020, The Generational Divide." https://www.medscape.com/slideshow/2020-lifestyle-burnout-6012460#2

43. Kane, Leslie, MA, "Medscape National Physician Burnout and Suicide Report 2020, The Generational Divide." https://www.medscape.com/slideshow/2020-lifestyle-burnout-6012460#5

44. Anderson, Pauline, "Doctor's Suicide Rate Highest of any Profession," Web MD, May 8, 2018. https://www.webmd.com/mental-health/news/20180508/doctors-suicide-rate-highest-of-any-profession

45. Andrew, Louise, MD, JD, "Physician Suicide," Medscape Aug 1, 2018. https://emedicine.medscape.com/article/806779-overview#a1

46. Wible, Pamela, MD, "What I've Learned From 1,513 Physician Suicides," Oct 18, 2017. https://www.idealmedicalcare.org/ive-learned-547-doctor-suicides/

47. Gunderman, Richard, MD, "How to Discourage a Doctor," The Health Care Blog, Sep 18, 2014. https://thehealthcareblog.com/blog/2014/09/18/how-to-discourage-a-doctor/

48. Fahrenkopf, AM, MD et al., "Rates of Medication Errors Among Depressed and Burnt Out Residents: Prospective Cohort Study", *BMJ*, Mar 1, 2008, 336 (7642) 448–451. https://www.ncbi.nlm.nih.gov/pmc/articles/PMC2258399/

49. Tawfik, D, MD, MS, et al., "Physician Burnout, Well Being and Work Unit Safety Grades in Relationship to Reported Medical Errors," Mayo Clinic Proceedings, Nov 1, 2018, Vol 93, Issue 11, 1571–1580. https://www.mayoclinicproceedings.org/article/S0025-6196(18)30372-0/fulltext

50. "What is Moral Injury," Moral Injury of Health Care LLC. https://fixmoralinjury.org/what-is-moral-injury/

51. Lopatin, M, MD, "Physicians Need to Shake Off Apathy and Advocate," *Bucks County Courier Times*, Jun 6, 2021. https://www.buckscountycouriertimes.com/story/opinion/2021/06/06/op-ed-physicians-need-shake-off-apathy-and-advocate/7508892002/

52. https://www.cnn.com/2001/LAW/06/13/elderabuse.lawsuit/index.html#:~:text=HAYWARD%2C%20California%20(CNN)%20%2D%2D,who%20later%20died%20of%20cancer.

53. "An Important View on Pain as the 5th Vital Sign," Pains Project. https://www.practicalbioethics.org/files/pains/PAINS-policy-brief-8.pdf

54. https://www.ama-assn.org/system/files/2020-06/prior-authorization-survey-2019.pdf

55. https://www.healio.com/news/primary-care/20180221/former-aetna-directors-admission-on-decision-process-could-impact-millions

56. https://www.cnn.com/2018/02/15/health/aetna-investigations-widen/index.html

57. https://www.goodrx.com/humira

58. "Appropriate use of Modifier 25," American College of Cardiology. https://www.acc.org/tools-and-practice-support/practice-solutions/coding-and-reimbursement/appropriate-use-of-modifier-25

59. "Modifier 25 – Frequently Asked Questions," Independence Provider News Center, Jul 24, 2017. https://provcomm.ibx.com/ibc/archive/pages/A86603B03881756B8525817E00768006.aspx

60. "PAMED Calls for Retroactive Delay of IBC's Modifier 25 Payment Policy," Pennsylvania Medical Society, Oct 2, 2017. https://www.pamedsoc.org/list/articles/Modifier-25-IBC

61. Stewart, A, "Anthem halts controversial modifier 25 reimbursement policy – 4 insights," *Becker's ASC Review*, Mar 2, 2018. https://www.beckersasc.com/asc-coding-billing-and-collections/anthem-halts-controversial-modifier-25-reimbursement-policy-4-insights.html

62. "What is Macra and What it Means to Providers and EHR Technology," EHRIntelligence, May 6, 2016. https://ehrintelligence.com/features/what-is-macra-and-what-it-means-to-providers-ehr-technology

63. "The Medicare Access and Chips Reauthorization Act," AAFP. https://www.aafp.org/family-physician/practice-and-career/getting-paid/macra.html

64. https://www.aafp.org/family-physician/practice-and-career/delivery-payment-models/direct-primary-care.html

65. Smith, G, "The Difference Between Direct Primary Care and Concierge Medicine," PeopleKeep, Feb 24, 2021. https://www.peoplekeep.com/blog/the-difference-between-direct-primary-care-and-concierge-medicine

66. "Understanding Drug Tiers," Patient Advocate Foundation. https://www.patientadvocate.org/explore-our-resources/understanding-health-insurance/understanding-drug-tiers/

67. https://www.medicareappeal.com/content/about-maximus-federal-services

68. Mangione, A, "The Multi-Billion Dollar Solution – Repeal Safe Harbor," Town Hall, Feb 3, 2018. https://townhall.com/columnists/andrewmangione/2018/03/03/the-multibillion-dollar-solution--repeal-safe-harbor-n2456781

69. United States Government Accountability Office Report to Congressional Requesters. GROUP PURCHASING ORGANIZATIONS Funding Structure Has Potential Implications for Medicare Costs, Oct 2014. https://www.gao.gov/assets/gao-15-13.pdf

70. Department of Health and Human Services Office of Inspector General, Fact Sheet: Federal Anti-Kickback Law and Regulatory Safe Harbors, (Washington, D.C., November 1999). https://oig.hhs.gov/fraud/docs/safeharborregulations/safefs.htm

71. https://oig.hhs.gov/fraud/docs/safeharborregulations/072991.htm

72. https://www.gao.gov/about

73. Singleton, M, MD, JD, "Group Purchasing Organizations – Gaming the System," *Journal of American Physicians and Surgeons*, Vol 23, No. 2, Summer 2018. https://www.jpands.org/vol23no2/singleton.pdf

74. Litan, RE, Singer, HJ, Birkenbach, A, "An Empirical Analysis of Aftermarket Transactions by Hospitals," *Journal of Contemporary Health Law and Policy*, Fall 2011, Vol 28, Issue 1. https://amac.us/wp-content/uploads/2018/03/journal-of-contemporary-health-law-and-policy.pdf

75. Bai, G, PhD, CPA, Sen A, PhD, Anderson, G, PhD, "Pharmaceutical Benefit Managers, Brand Name Drug Prices, and Patient Cost Sharing," *Annals of Internal Medicine*, Feb 13, 2018, 436–438. https://www.acpjournals.org/doi/abs/10.7326/m17-2506

76. Coppock, K, MA, "Legislation Signed Into Law Prohibiting 'Gag Clauses' for Pharmacies," *Pharmacy Times*, Oct 13, 2018. https://www.pharmacytimes.com/view/legislation-signed-into-law-prohibiting-gag-clauses-for-pharmacies

77. https://www.physiciansagainstdrugshortages.com/gpo-facts--pay-to-play-.html

78. https://nebula.wsimg.com/c3d3739b1126263421379b3bf639752c?AccessKeyId=62BC662C928C06F7384C&disposition=0&alloworigin=1

79. Vandervelde A, Blalock E, "The Pharmaceutical Supply Chain, Gross Drug Expenditures Realized by Stakeholders." https://ecommunications.thinkbrg.com/44/1664/uploads/vandervelde-phrma-january-2020.3.3-addendum-clean.pdf?intIaContactId=KhZpazvOsWW2krAvO0096w%3d%3d&intExternalSystemId=1

80. United States Government Accountability Office Report to Congressional Requesters. "DRUG SHORTAGES Public Health Threat Continues, Despite Efforts to

Help Ensure Product Availability," Feb 2014. https://www.gao.gov/assets/gao-14-194.pdf

81. Mazer-Amirshahi, M, Pharm. D., MD, MPH, Fox, ER, Pharm D, "Saline Shortages – Many Causes, No Simple Solution," *NEJM*, Apr 19, 2018, 378:1472–1474. https://www.nejm.org/doi/full/10.1056/NEJMp1800347

82. https://www.physiciansagainstdrugshortages.com/congressional-hearings.html

83. Bogdanich, W, Meier, B, Walsh, MW, "Medicine's Middlemen; Questions Raised of Conflicts at 2 Hospital Buying Groups" *New York Times*, Mar 4, 2002. https://www.nytimes.com/2002/03/04/business/medicine-s-middlemen-questions-raised-of-conflicts-at-2-hospital-buying-groups.html

84. Scanlon, WJ, Director Health Care Issues, Testimony Before the Subcommittee on Antitrust, Competition, and Business and Consumer Rights, Committee on the Judiciary, U.S. Senate, "GROUP PURCHASING ORGANIZATIONS – Pilot Study Suggests Large Buying Groups Do Not Always Offer Hospitals Lower Prices," Apr 30, 2002. https://www.gao.gov/assets/gao-02-690t.pdf

85. GAO@100. "GROUP PURCHASING ORGANIZATIONS – Pilot Study Suggests Large Buying Groups Do Not Always Offer Hospitals Lower Prices," Apr 30, 2002. https://www.gao.gov/products/gao-02-690t

86. https://www.ftc.gov/news-events/audio-video/video/understanding-competition-prescription-drug-markets-panel-3 1:13.20

87. United States Government Accountability Office Report to Congressional Requesters. "GROUP PURCHASING ORGANIZATIONS Funding Structure Has Potential Implications for Medicare Costs," Oct 2014, 19–20. https://www.gao.gov/assets/gao-15-13.pdf

88. AMA Board Response/Action on Resolution to Oppose Safe Harbor Exemptions for PBMs.

89. Hinsdale, JG, MD, Chair of the AMA Council on Medical Services, REPORT 8 (A-19) Group Purchasing Organizations and Pharmacy Benefit Manager Safe Harbor (Reference Committee G). https://www.ama-assn.org/system/files/2019-07/a19-cms-report-8.pdf

90. Kohn, LT, Director of Health Care, GAO, Letter to Senator Charles Grassley, "Group Purchasing Organizations: Research on Their Pricing Impact on Health Care Providers," Jan 29, 2010. https://www.gao.gov/assets/gao-10-323r.pdf

91. Gottlieb, S, Keynote Address at the 2018 Food and Drug Law Institute Annual Conference, May 3, 2018. https://www.fda.gov/news-events/speeches-fda-officials/keynote-address-2018-fdli-annual-conference-05032018

92. The Federal Register, Executive Order 13939 of July 24, 2020, "Lowering Prices for Patients by Eliminating Kickbacks to Middlemen," Jul 29, 2020. https://www.federalregister.gov/documents/2020/07/29/2020-16625/lowering-prices-for-patients-by-eliminating-kickbacks-to-middlemen

93. Baker Ober Health Law, "HHS/OIG Finalizes Rule Stripping PBM Rebates of Safe Harbor Protection," Dec 3, 2020. https://www.jdsupra.com/legalnews/hhs-oig-finalizes-rule-stripping-pbm-87734/

94. "Fraud and Abuse; Removal of Safe Harbor Protection for Rebates Involving Prescription Pharmaceuticals and Creation of New Safe Harbor Protection for Certain Point-of-Sale Reductions in Price on Prescription Pharmaceuticals and Certain Pharmacy Benefit Manager Service Fees; Additional Delayed Effective Date," *Federal Register*, Mar 22, 2021. https://www.federalregister.gov/documents/2021/03/22/2021-05903/fraud-and-abuse-removal-of-safe-harbor-protection-for-rebates-involving-prescription-pharmaceuticals

95. "Medicare and State Health Care Programs: Fraud and Abuse; Revisions to Safe Harbors Under the Anti-Kickback Statute, and Civil Monetary Penalty Rules Regarding Beneficiary Inducements," *Federal Register*, Dec 2, 2020. https://www.federalregister.gov/documents/2020/12/02/2020-26072/medicare-and-state-health-care-programs-fraud-and-abuse-revisions-to-safe-harbors-under-the

96. Federal Register Rules and Regulations, Nov 30, 2020. https://www.govinfo.gov/content/pkg/FR-2020-11-30/pdf/2020-25841.pdf, p4

97. Fisher, WB, MD, Schloss, EJ, MD, "Medical specialty certification in the United States–a false idol?", *Journal of Interventional Cardiac Electrophysiology*, Mar 8, 2016, 47(1): 37–43. https://www.ncbi.nlm.nih.gov/pmc/articles/PMC5045479/#CR5

98. Flexner, A. (2015) "Medical Education in the United States and Canada: A Report to the Carnegie Foundation for the Advancement of Teaching," 1910. http://archive.carnegiefoundation.org/publications/pdfs/elibrary/Carnegie_Flexner_Report.pdf

99. Duffy, TP, MD. "The Flexner report – 100 years later," *Yale Journal of Biology and Medicine*, Sep 8, 2011 84(3): 269–276. https://www.ncbi.nlm.nih.gov/pmc/articles/PMC3178858/

100. Cassel, CK, MD, and Holmboe, ES, "Professionalism and Accountability: The Role of Specialty Board Certification," Transactions of the American Clinical and Climatologic Association. 2008; 119: 295–304. https://www.ncbi.nlm.nih.gov/pmc/articles/PMC2394686/

101. "The American Board of Internal Medicine," *British Medical Journal*, Aug 29, 1936 (3947): 439–440. https://www.bmj.com/content/2/3947/439.2

102. https://www.abms.org/about-abms/

103. https://www.abms.org/board-certification/

104. https://www.abim.org/about/mission/

105. Sandhu, AT, MD, Adams Dudley, R, MD, MBA, Kazi, DS, MD, Msc, MS, "A Cost Analysis of the American Board of Internal Medicine's Maintenance-of-Certification Program," *Annals of Internal Medicine*, Sep 15, 2015. https://www.acpjournals.org/doi/10.7326/M15-1011?articleID=2398911

106. https://nbpas.org/about-nbpas/

107. Teirstein, PS, MD, "Boarded to Death – Why Maintenance of Certification is Bad for Doctors and Patients," *NEJM*, Jan 8, 2015, 372: 106–108. https://www.nejm.org/doi/full/10.1056/nejmp1407422

108. https://nbpas.org/wp-content/uploads/2018/06/MOC-Journal-Club_2018-05-30.pdf

109. Hayes, J, MD, Jackson JL, MD, McNutt, GM, MD, "Association Between Physician Time-Unlimited vs. Time-Limited Internal Medicine Board Certification and Ambulatory Patient Care Quality," *JAMA*, Dec 10, 2014; 312(22): 2358–2363. https://jamanetwork.com/journals/jama/fullarticle/2020370?resultClick=3

110. Letter from Rich Baron, MD, MACP, President and CEO of ABIM, "ABIM Announces Immediate Changes to MOC Program," Feb 3, 2015. https://www.abim.org/media-center/press-releases/abim-announces-immediate-changes-to-moc-program.aspx

111. Ault, A, "ABIM on MOC: We Got It Wrong," Medscape, Feb 3, 2015. https://www.medscape.com/viewarticle/839178

112. Eichenwald, K, "The Ugly Civil War in American Medicine," *Newsweek*, Mar 10, 2015. https://www.newsweek.com/2015/03/27/ugly-civil-war-american-medicine-312662.html

113. Eichenwald, K, "A Certified Medical Controversy," *Newsweek*, Apr 7, 2015. https://www.newsweek.com/certified-medical-controversy-320495

114. Eichenwald, K, "To the Barricades! The Doctors Revolt Against ABIM is Succeeding," *Newsweek*, Sep 15, 2015. https://www.newsweek.com/abim-american-board-internal-medicine-doctors-revolt-372723

115. Fisher, WG, MD, "The ABIM Foundation: Choosing Wisely and the $2.3 Million Condominium," Dr. Wes Blog Spot, Dec 16, 2014. http://drwes.blogspot.com/2014/12/the-abim-foundation-choosing-wisely-and.html

116. "AMA Adopts Principles for Maintenance of Certification," Nov 10 2014. https://www.ama-assn.org/education/cme/ama-adopts-principles-maintenance-certification

117. https://nbpas.org/wp-content/Downloads/PAMED%20no%20confidece%20in%20ABIM.pdf

118. Position Statement on Maintenance of Certification, American College of Rheumatology, Aug 2015. https://www.rheumatology.org/Portals/0/Files/ACR%20MOC%20Postion%20Statement%202015.pdf

119. Walsh, N, "ACR Joins Outcry Against ABIM's MOC Program," MedPage Today, Aug 28, 2015. https://www.medpagetoday.com/rheumatology/general rheumatology/53280

120. http://www.medtees.com/content/ABIMAppellateDecision.pdf

121. Bendix, J, "ABIM Cleared of Antitrust Charges," *Medical Economics*, Oct 4, 2019. https://www.medicaleconomics.com/view/abim-cleared-antitrust-charges

122. Fisher, WG, MD, "The Courts Speak: Internists to be Boarded to Death," Dr. Wes Blog Spot, Mar 1, 2021. http://drwes.blogspot.com/

123. Fisher, WG, MD, "ABIM First Time MOC Pass Rates 2000–2014," Dr. Wes Blog Spot, Sep 25, 2015. http://drwes.blogspot.com/2015/09/abim-first-time-moc-pass-rates-2000-2014.html

124. http://www.medtees.com/images/InternalMedicinePassRatebyYear.png

125. https://www.abim.org/maintenance-of-certification/assessment-information/assessment-options/longitudinal-knowledge-assessment/

126. Yurkiewicz, S, "MOC Watch: MOC Care Quality Unhanged by New Rules – MOC Makes No Difference in Primary Care Patient Outcomes," MedPage Today, Jan 4, 2015. https://www.medpagetoday.com/publichealthpolicy/medicaleducation/49369

127. https://m.facebook.com/62316799226/posts/10158563830539227/?d=n&substory_index=0

128. Hackethal, V, MD, Msc, "Physician Organizations Challenge PA Name Change," MedPage Today, Jun 9, 2021. https://www.medpagetoday.com/special-reports/exclusives/93007

129. Bailey, SR, MD, "Statement on AAPA change of 'Physician Assistant' Title," Jun 3, 2021. https://www.ama-assn.org/press-center/ama-statements/statement-aapa-change-physician-assistant-title

130. Lopatin, M, MD, "A Plea For Transparency in Medicine," *Bucks County Courier Times*, Nov 4, 2020. https://www.buckscountycouriertimes.com/story/

opinion/columns/your-voice/2020/11/05/guest-opinion-plea-transparency-practice-medicine/6161991002/

131. Dufevelt, H, MD, "The Implications of Provider vs. Doctor," Kevin MD, Apr 13, 2012. https://www.kevinmd.com/blog/2012/04/implications-provider-doctor.html

132. "Provider, Use of Term," AAFP Position Paper. https://www.aafp.org/about/policies/all/provider.html

133. Hartzband, P, MD, Groopman J, MD, "The New Language of Medicine," *NEJM*, Oct 13, 2011, 365: 1372–1373. https://www.nejm.org/doi/full/10.1056/NEJMp1107278

134. Saenger, P, MD, "Jewish Pediatricians in Nazi Germany: Victims of Persecution," *IMAJ*, May 2006, Vol. 8, 324–328. https://www.ima.org.il/FilesUploadPublic/IMAJ/0/48/24103.pdf

135. Al-Agba, N, MD, "If You Call Me Provider, I Will Assume You Are a Nazi," The Deductible. Feb 8, 2019. https://thedeductible.com/2019/02/08/if-you-call-me-a-provider-i-will-assume-you-are-a-nazi/

136. https://www.merriam-webster.com/

137. Vestal, C, "Nurse Practitioners Slowly Gain Autonomy," Kaiser Health News, Jul 19, 2013. https://khn.org/news/stateline-nurse-practitioners-scope-of-practice/

138. https://www.aanp.org/advocacy/state/state-practice-environment

139. "PAMED Coalition Opposition to Senate Bill 25," Jun 15, 2021. https://www.pamedsoc.org/docs/librariesprovider2/pamed-documents/advocacy-priorities/physician-coalition-letter_oppose-sb-25_061521.pdf?sfvrsn=81707a58_3

140. AAFP Backgrounder – "Education and Training – Family Physicians versus Nurse Practitioners." https://www.aafp.org/dam/AAFP/documents/advocacy/workforce/scope/FPvsNP.pdf

141. https://www.nccwebsite.org/content/documents/cms/2020323_final_statement_np_students_and_clinical_hours.pdf

142. Primary Care Coalition, "Compare the Education Gaps Between Primary Care Physicians and Nurse Practitioners." https://www.tafp.org/Media/Default/Downloads/advocacy/scope-education.pdf

143. Al-Agba, N, MD, Bernard, R, MD, "Patients at Risk – The Rise of the Nurse Practitioner and Physician Assistant in Health Care," 2020, 20–21. https://www.patientsatrisk.com/

144. https://www.aapa.org/career-central/become-a-pa/

145. Link PAs, "Nursing Model vs. Medical Model (Similarities and Differences)." https://linkpas.com/nursing-vs-medical-model/

146. https://nursing-theory.org/articles/Nursing_care_plans_in_action.php

147. Sackett, DL, MD, MSc, Spitzer, WO, MD, MHA, MPH, "The Burlington Randomized Trial of the Nurse Practitioner: Health Outcomes of Patients," *Annals of Internal Medicine*, Feb, 1974, Vol. 80, No. 2, 137–142. https://citeseerx.ist.psu.edu/viewdoc/download?doi=10.1.1.855.177&rep=rep1&type=pdf

148. DeCapua, M, DNP, PMHNP, "Let's Settle This Once and For All: Do Nurse Practitioners Provide Patient Care Equal to That of Physicians?", Health eCareers, Jun 11, 2019. https://www.healthecareers.com/article/career/nurse-practitioners-provide-patient-care-equal-to-that-of-physicians

149. "Quality of Nurse Practitioner Practice," American Association of Nurse Practitioners. https://www.aanp.org/advocacy/advocacy-resource/position-statements/quality-of-nurse-practitioner-practice

150. Al-Agba, N, MD, Bernard, R, MD, "Patients at Risk – The Rise of the Nurse Practitioner and Physician Assistant in Health Care," 2020, xvi–xvii. https://www.patientsatrisk.com/

151. Al-Agba, N, MD, Bernard, R, MD, "Patients at Risk – The Rise of the Nurse Practitioner and Physician Assistant in Health Care," 2020, 104–128. https://www.patientsatrisk.com/

152. "Open Letter to the AMA, AAEM and AAEMRSA," Jul 10, 2019. https://www.aanp.org/news-feed/open-letter-to-the-ama-aaem-and-aaem-rsa

153. https://www.google.com/search?sxsrf=ALeKk02BF2US3pqpzut1C2mZS0Z0q-daICA:1625349219414&source=univ&tbm=isch&q=heart+of+a+nurse+brain+of+a+doctor+advertisement&sa=X&ved=2ahUKEwjFr-_W8cfxAhXYbc0K-HYnQAs0QjJkEegQIBxAC&biw=1536&bih=760&dpr=1.25

154. Pennsylvania Senate Bill 25. https://legiscan.com/PA/text/SB25/2021

155. Jauhar, S, MD, "Nurses are Not Doctors," *New York Times*, Apr 29, 2014. https://www.nytimes.com/2014/04/30/opinion/nurses-are-not-doctors.html?fbclid=I-wAR0wXhdmTEwklJTjn4WkAubIw_XXeJ8HzKPiBGo-OhitoC8pAeBwmb-FOOkw

156. Drum, K, "The AMA Represents Only About One-Sixth of Physicians," *Mother Jones*, Dec 27, 2016. https://www.motherjones.com/kevin-drum/2016/12/ama-represents-only-about-one-sixth-all-doctors/

157. Campbell, K, MD, "Don't Believe AMA's Hype, Membership Still Declining," MedPage Today, Jun 19, 2019. https://www.medpagetoday.com/opinion/campbells-scoop/80583

158. Herzog, A, MD, Chair of the AMA Council on Long-Range Planning and Development, "Demographic Characteristics of the House of Delegates and AMA Leadership," 2019, 4. https://www.ama-assn.org/system/files/2019-08/a19-clrpd-report-1.pdf

159. Madara, J, MD, "AMA Membership Growth a Sign That Physicians Demand Change," Jun 19, 2021. https://www.ama-assn.org/about/leadership/ama-membership-growth-sign-physicians-demand-change

160. Girgis, L, MD, "Is the AMA Really the Voice of Physicians in the U.S.," *Physicians Weekly*, Jun 9, 2015. https://www.physiciansweekly.com/is-the-ama-really-the-voice-of-physicians-in-the-us

161. Pearlstein, S, "Donald Trump is about to face a rude awakening over Obamacare," *Washington Post*, Nov 12, 2016. https://www.washingtonpost.com/news/wonk/wp/2016/11/12/donald-trump-is-beginning-to-face-a-rude-awakening-over-obamacare/

162. Norris, L, "Is There Still a Penalty for Being Uninsured in 2021?", *Verywell Health*, Nov 22, 2020. https://www.verywellhealth.com/obamacare-penalty-for-being-uninsured-4132434#:~:text=The%20ACA's%20individual%20mandate%20penalty,be%20the%20case%20for%202021

163. Talgo, C, "ObamaCare: 10 Years of Distress and Disappointment," *The Hill*, Mar 5, 2020. https://thehill.com/opinion/healthcare/486134-obamacare-10-years-of-distress-and-disappointment

164. Kominski, GF, Nonzee, NJ, Sorensen, A, "The Affordable Care Act's Impacts on Access to Insurance and Health Care for Low-Income Populations," *Annual Review of Public Health*, Mar 2017, Vol 38, 489–505. https://www.annualreviews.org/doi/full/10.1146/annurev-publhealth-031816-044555

165. Glied, S, PhD, Ma, S, Borja, A, "Effect of the Affordable Care Act on Health Care Access," Issue Brief, Commonwealth Fund, May 13, 2017, 1–11. https://pubmed.ncbi.nlm.nih.gov/28574234/#affiliation-1

166. Blumenthal, D, Collins, SR, Fowler, E, "The Affordable Care Act at 10 Years: What's the Effect on Health Care Coverage and Access?", The Commonwealth Fund, Feb 26, 2020. https://www.commonwealthfund.org/publications/journal-article/2020/feb/aca-at-10-years-effect-health-care-coverage-access

167. Garfield, R, Orgera, K, Damico, A, "The Uninsured and the ACA: A Primer – Key Facts About Health Insurance and the Uninsured Amidst Changes to the Affordable Care Act," Kaiser Family Foundation, Jan 25 2019. https://www.kff.org/report-section/the-uninsured-and-the-aca-a-primer-key-facts-about-health-insurance-and-the-uninsured-amidst-changes-to-the-affordable-care-act-how-does-lack-of-insurance-affect-access-to-care/

168. Roland, J, "The Pros and Cons of Obamacare," Healthline, Aug 16, 2019. https://www.healthline.com/health/consumer-healthcare-guide/pros-and-cons-obamacare#pros

169. Mills, D, "Is It True? Do Doctors Really Loathe Obamacare?", Healthline, Aug 1, 2019. https://www.healthline.com/health-news/do-doctors-loathe-obamacare-041415#Chief-Complaints-Concern-Payments

170. https://physiciansfoundation.org/

171. Hamel, L, Kirzinger, A, et al., "5 Charts About Public Opinion on the Affordable Care Act and the Supreme Court," Kaiser Family Foundation, Dec 18, 2020. https://www.kff.org/health-reform/poll-finding/5-charts-about-public-opinion-on-the-affordable-care-act-and-the-supreme-court/

172. "A 2014 survey of America's Physicians," The Physician's Foundation, Sep 2014. https://physiciansfoundation.org/wpcontent/uploads/2017/12/2014_Physicians_Foundation_Biennial_Physician_Survey_Report.pdf

173. Graham, J, "Like a Slap in the Face: Doctors No Longer Feel The Nation's Largest Doctor Group Represents Their Interests," Business Insider, Dec 22, 2016. https://www.businessinsider.com/doctors-american-medical-association-2016-12

174. Japsen, B, "AMA: Build on the ACA Rather Than Pursue Medicare For All," *Forbes*, Jun 11, 2019. https://www.forbes.com/sites/brucejapsen/2019/06/11/ama-balks-at-supporting-single-payer-medicare-for-all/?sh=58432fd065f1

175. Carr, D, "Why Doctors Are Fighting Their Professional Organization Over Medicare For All," *The Nation*, Feb 24, 2020. https://www.thenation.com/article/politics/ama-medicare-insurance/

176. "ICD 10 Codes for Gout," DocCharge. https://doccharge.com/blog/icd-10-codes-for-gout/

177. "2020 Annual AMA Report" p 19. https://www.ama-assn.org/system/files/2021-04/2020-annual-report.pdf

178. Hunt, B, "AMA? BITFD!", *Epsilon Theory*, Nov 24, 2020. https://www.epsilontheory.com/ama-bitfd/

179. "Medicare Sustainable Growth Rate." https://en.wikipedia.org/wiki/Medicare_Sustainable_Growth_Rate

180. Ryan, C, "Explaining the Medicare Sustainable Growth Rate," American Action Forum, Mar 26, 2015. https://www.americanactionforum.org/insight/explaining-the-medicare-sustainable-growth-rate/#_ftn6

181. Steinbrook, R, MD, "The Repeal of Medicare's Sustainable Growth Rate for Physician Payment," *JAMA*, May 26, 2015, 313(20): 2025–2026. https://jamanetwork.com/journals/jama/fullarticle/2277734

182. https://www.cms.gov/Medicare/Quality-Initiatives-Patient-Assessment-Instruments/Value-Based-Programs/MACRA-MIPS-and-APMs/MACRA-MIPS-and-APMs

183. Cheryl, "The Two Sides of Macra: Examining the Pros and Cons," MD Audit, Aug 10, 2016. https://www.hayesmanagement.com/the-two-sides-of-macra-examining-the-pros-and-cons/

184. Casalino, L, "The Medicare Access and CHIP Reauthorization Act and the Corporate Transformation of American Medicine," *Health Affairs*, May 2017, Vol. 36, No. 5. https://www.healthaffairs.org/doi/10.1377/hlthaff.2016.1536

185. LaPointe, J, "AMA Voices Concerns Over Macra Implementation, MIPS, APMs," *RevCycleIntelligence*, Jun 29, 2016. https://revcycleintelligence.com/news/ama-voices-concerns-over-macra-implementation-mips-apms

186. Twachtman, G, "Docs to CMS: Macra is Too Complex and Should be Delayed," *GI & Hepatology News*, July 9, 2016. https://www.mdedge.com/gihepnews/article/110255/health-policy/docs-cms-macra-too-complex-and-should-be-delayed

187. Sprey, E, "The Inbox: Physicians Deliberations on Macra," Physicians Practice, May 30, 2016. https://www.physicianspractice.com/view/inbox-physician-deliberations-macra

188. https://practicingphysician.org/

189. https://www.physiciansworkingtogether.org/

190. https://www.physiciansagainstdrugshortages.com/

191. https://www.physiciansforpatientprotection.org/

192. https://free2care.org/

193. "Free2Care Press Release: Coalition Responds to WSJ Press Release Regarding AMA." http://free2care.org/free2care-press-release-coalition-responds-to-wsj-editorial-board-piece-regarding-ama/

194. "Reducing Cost and Waste in American Medicine A Physician-Led Roadmap to Patient-Centered Medical Care Symposium," Apr 2019. http://free2care.org/wp-content/uploads/2020/07/Free2care.pdf

195. Lopatin, M, MD, "Will Covid Stop the Devaluation of Physicians?", Kevin MD, Apr 1, 2020. https://www.kevinmd.com/blog/2020/04/will-covid-19-stop-the-devaluation-of-physicians.html

196. Al-Arshani, S, "Nurse dies in New York hospital where workers are reduced to using trash bags as protective medical gear," *Business Insider*, Mar 26, 2020. https://www.businessinsider.com/kious-kelly-hospital-nurse-dies-trash-bags-2020-3?fbclid=IwAR0Trn3CU_xrbcsxykfTXQbUE1hnSVvRsax5R_GUMyd-D55MfrSiLN-D8wA

197. Ault, A, "Amid PPE Shortage, Clinicians Face Harassment, Firing for Self-Care," Medscape, Mar 26, 2020. https://www.medscape.com/viewarticle/927590

198. Gstalter, M, "Doctor Who Criticized Hospital's Measures Against Coronavirus is Fired," *The Hill*, Mar 28, 2020. https://thehill.com/blogs/blog-briefing-room/news/489969-doctor-who-criticized-hospitals-measures-against-coronavirus-is

199. Reno, J, "Why PPE Is Still in Short Supply for Healthcare Workers," Healthline, Dec 5, 2020. https://www.healthline.com/health-news/why-ppe-is-still-in-short-supply-for-healthcareworkers#:~:text=Healthcare%20workers%20say%20personal%20protective,supply%20isn't%20meeting%20demand.

200. "CMS Announces Relief for Clinicians, Providers, Hospitals and Facilities Participating in Quality Reporting Programs in Response to COVID-19," Centers for Medicare and Medicaid Services, Mar 22, 2020. https://www.cms.gov/newsroom/press-releases/cms-announces-relief-clinicians-providers-hospitals-and-facilities-participating-quality-reporting.

201. Ebbs, S, "Trump Announces Potential Game Changer on Drugs to Treat Novel Corona Virus, But FDA Says More Study is Needed," ABC News, Mar 19, 2020. https://abcnews.go.com/Politics/trump-announces-potential-game-changer-drugs-treat-covid19/story?id=69693560

202. Wemple, E, "Opinion: From Fox News, A Big Dose of Dumb on Hydroxychloroquine," *Washington Post*, Apr 23, 2020. https://www.washingtonpost.com/opinions/2020/04/23/why-are-fox-news-opinion-hosts-so-wrong-about-hydroxychloroquine/

203. Tucker Carlson, 4/3/20, referring to HCQ as a possible treatment.

204. Molina, JM, Delaugerre, C, et al., "No evidence of rapid antiviral clearance or clinical benefit with the combination of hydroxychloroquine and azithromycin in patients with severe COVID-19 infection," *Médecine et Maladies Infectieuses*, Jun 2020, Vol. 50, Issue 4, 384.

205. Magagnoli, J, MS, Narendran, S, MD, et al., "Outcomes of Hydroxychloroquine Usage in United States Veterans Hospitalized With Covid 19," MedRxiv, Apr 21, 2020. https://www.medrxiv.org/content/10.1101/2020.04.16.20065920v1.full.pdf

206. Million, M, Lagier, J, et al., "Early treatment of COVID-19 patients with hydroxychloroquine and azithromycin: A retrospective analysis of 1061 cases in Marseille, France," *Travel Medicine and Infectious Disease*, (2020) 35, May 5, 2020. https://www.mediterranee-infection.com/wp-content/uploads/2020/04/MS.pdf

207. Lopatin, M, MD, "The Hydroxychloroquine Quandary," *Physician Outlook*, Jun 10, 2020. https://www.physicianoutlook.com/articles/hydroxychloroquine-quandary

208. Hoekstra, K, "Opinion: Michigan Doctors Fight Corona Virus and Governor's Office," *The Detroit News*, Mar 26, 2020. https://www.detroitnews.com/story/

opinion/2020/03/26/opinion-michigans-doctors-fight-coronavirus-and-governors-office/2922272001/

209. "Reminder of Appropriate Prescribing and Dispensing," Department of Licensing and Regulatory Affairs, State of Michigan, Mar 24, 2020. https://www.michigan.gov/documents/lara/Reminder_of_Appropriate_Prescribing_and_Dispensing_3-24-2020_684869_7.pdf

210. Devito, L, "Gov. Whitmer Reverses Course on Coronavirus Drugs, Is Now Asking Feds For Hydroxychloroquine and Chloroquine," *Detroit Metro Times*, Apr 20, 2020. https://www.metrotimes.com/news-hits/archives/2020/03/31/gov-whitmer-reverses-course-on-coronavirus-drugs-is-now-asking-feds-for-hydroxychloroquine-and-chloroquine

211. Murray, S, MD, "New Jersey Restricts Prescribing Medicines Used to Treat Covid," *Pharmacy Times*, Apr 2, 2020. https://www.pharmacytimes.com/news/new-jersey-restricts-prescribing-medicines-used-to-treat-covid-19

212. https://en.wikipedia.org/wiki/America's_Frontline_Doctors

213. Funke, D, "Don't Fall for This Video: Hydroxychloroquine is Not a Covid Cure," PolitiFact, Jul 28, 2020. https://www.politifact.com/factchecks/2020/jul/28/stella-immanuel/dont-fall-video-hydroxychloroquine-not-covid-19-cu/

214. Dupuy, B, "Video Falsely Touts Hydroxychloroquine as COVID-19 Cure," Associated Press, July 28, 2020. https://apnews.com/article/fact-checking-9153030274

215. Passantino, J, and Darcy, O, "Social Media Giants Remove Viral Video With False Coronavirus Claims That Trump Retweeted," CNN Business, Jul 28, 2020. https://www.cnn.com/2020/07/28/tech/facebook-youtube-coronavirus/index.html

216. Colvin, J, O'Brien, M, "Trump Files Suit Against Facebook, Twitter and YouTube," Associated Press, Jul 7, 2021. https://apnews.com/article/lawsuits-business-government-and-politics-c7e26858dcb553f92d98706d12ad510c

217. Lopatin, M, MD, "Regarding HCQ," *Bucks/Montgomery Physician*, Fall 2020, 8–10. https://www.nxtbook.com/hoffmann/BucksMontgomeryPhysician/BucksMontFall2020/index.php#/p/10

218. Bernazzani, S, "The Importance of Considering the Social Determinants of Health," *American Journal of Managed Care*, May 1, 2016. https://www.ajmc.com/view/the-importance-of-considering-the-social-determinants-of-health

219. Artiga, S, Hinton, E, "Beyond Health Care: The Role of Social Determinants in Promoting Health and Health Equity," Kaiser Family Foundation, May 10, 2018. https://www.kff.org/racial-equity-and-health-policy/issue-brief/beyond-health-care-the-role-of-social-determinants-in-promoting-health-and-health-equity/

220. https://www.hhs.gov/sites/default/files/cms-1717-f2.pdf

221. "Hospital Price Transparency," Centers for Medicare and Medicaid Services. https://www.cms.gov/hospital-price-transparency

222. "Semi-Annual Hospital Price Transparency Compliance Report, July 2021," Patient Rights Advocate.org. https://static1.squarespace.com/static/60065b-8fc8cd610112ab89a7/t/60f1c225e1a54c0e42272fbf/1626456614723/Patient-RightsAdvocate.org+Semi-Annual+Hospital+Compliance+Report.pdf

223. https://www.cadc.uscourts.gov/internet/opinions.nsf/CCDF215AF-CAF25F98525864D005716BC/$file/20-5193-1877500.pdf

224. https://casetext.com/case/am-hosp-assn-v-azar-8

225. https://www.patientrightsadvocate.org/

226. "HHS Finalizes Rule Requiring Manufacturers Disclose Drug Prices in TV Ads to Increase Drug Pricing Transparency," U.S Department of Health and Human Services, May 8, 2019. https://public3.pagefreezer.com/browse/HHS.gov/31-12-2020T08:51/https://www.hhs.gov/about/news/2019/05/08/hhs-finalizes-rule-requiring-manufacturers-disclose-drug-prices-in-tv-ads.html

227. "Court Rules Trump Can't Require Drugmakers To Disclose Prices in TV Ads," Associated Press, Jun 18, 2020. https://fortune.com/2020/06/18/prescription-drug-prices-tv-ads/

228. https://www.youtube.com/watch?v=AGyZtPctTsg

229. https://www.humira.com/cost

230. "Surprise Medical Bills: New Protections for Consumers Take Effect in 2022," Kaiser Family Foundation, Feb 4, 2020. https://www.kff.org/private-insurance/fact-sheet/surprise-medical-bills-new-protections-for-consumers-take-effect-in-2022/

231. "HHS Announces Rule to Protect Consumers from Surprise Medical Bills," Department of Health and Human Services, Jul 1, 2021. https://www.hhs.gov/about/news/2021/07/01/hhs-announces-rule-to-protect-consumers-from-surprise-medical-bills.html

232. "Understanding Facility Fees," The Alliance. https://the-alliance.org/wp-content/uploads/2021/05/Understanding_Facility_Fees_TA114-0116.pdf

233. Jameson Carey, M, "Facility Fees: The Farce Everyone Pays For," *Medical Economics*, Aug 16, 2018. https://www.aid-us.org/resources/Documents/Facility%20fees_the%20farce%20everyone%20pays%20for.pdf

234. O'Neil, M, "Same Surgery, Different Price: New Rules Could Improve Healthcare Price Transparency | Opinion," *The Tennessean*, Mar 30, 2021. https://www.tennessean.com/story/opinion/2021/03/30/new-federal-rules-could-improve-health-care-price-transparency/7054439002/

235. Weber, L, "Her Doctor's Office Moved 1 Floor Up. Why Did Her Treatment Cost 10 Times More?" NPR, Mar 26, 2021. https://www.npr.org/sections/health-shots/2021/03/26/976112513/her-doctors-office-moved-1-floor-up-why-did-her-treatment-cost-10-times-more

236. Feeney, C, "Remember Cunningham's plea? The same goes for Wentz in this Eagles season," NBC Sports, Nov 17, 2020. https://www.nbcsports.com/philadelphia/eagles/randall-cunningham-plea-same-goes-carson-wentz-2020-eagles-season

Acknowledgments

The boards of trustees of both PAMED and MCMS for their dedicated commitment to physicians and patients.

The staff at PAMED for their tireless work that so often is not acknowledged adequately. I cannot begin to thank them enough.

Marty Raniowski for his administrative skills as the executive vice president of PAMED.

Dave Thompson for his expertise in legislative affairs and his willingness to share that with me time after time.

Marty Trichtinger for his political expertise and tutelage.

Chuck Cutler, Scott Shapiro, and Wes Fisher for their leadership in promoting reform of MOC.

Niran Al-Agba and Rebekah Bernard for their exhaustive work on scope of practice.

Bob Campbell and Phil Zweig for their persistence in pushing for repeal of the safe harbor exemption for GPOs and PBMs.

Kim Jackson for her work in PWT in helping to bring physicians together.

Pamela Wible for her efforts in the area of moral injury and physician suicide.

Marni Jameson Carey for her advocacy in support of independent physicians.

Marion Mass for her tenacity and for her inspiration as a model for how health-care advocacy should be done. More importantly, for her friendship.

PPP for speaking out loudly regarding scope of practice concerns

Other health-care advocates—there are far too many to name individually. I thank all of you for your courage in speaking out and the countless hours you spend fighting to improve health care for patients. I thank you for your camaraderie and the friendships I have formed as we fight for a common cause.

Rheumatic Disease Associates—my family away from home for 28 years.

John Anastasia and Shane Fitzgerald for their repeated willingness to publish my op-eds in the *Bucks County Courier Times*.

My patients for allowing me to travel life's roads with them.

My daughter Dana for her proofreading assistance. I now know what an Oxford comma is.

Kot copyediting and proofreading for their professional expertise. Their superior editing skills have greatly improved this book.

Jeff Young, PhD from Universal Publishing for his assistance in making this book a reality.

But mostly, Suzan, Dana, and Melanie for their unending love, patience, and support of my endeavors.

Lightning Source UK Ltd.
Milton Keynes UK
UKHW022127180122
397356UK00007B/1565